BAYOU BEND

Bayou Bend, built 1927, garden façade.

BAYOU BEND

American Furniture, Paintings and Silver from the Bayou Bend Collection

By David B. Warren

With a foreword by Miss Ima Hogg

The Museum of Fine Arts, Houston

Distributed by New York Graphic Society Ltd.

Library of Congress Catalog Card Number 74–27648
ISBN 0–316–08401–8 (clothbound)
ISBN 89090–000–0 (paperbound)
Published by The Museum of Fine Arts, Houston
Cloth edition published by
New York Graphic Society, 11 Beacon St., Boston, Mass. 02108
Printed in the United States of America

Contents

Foreword

By Miss Ima Hogg

The Bayou Bend Collection was always designed for the public. From the time I acquired my first country Queen Anne armchair in 1920, I had an unaccountable compulsion to make an American collection for some Texas museum.

I presented this idea to my eldest brother, William C. Hogg, as an opportunity. Always an ardent ally for anything he felt was good for Texas, he saw the point at once and was ever truly interested as long as he lived.

There were few reliable sources of information at this time. It was some years before Wallace Nutting compiled his indispensable publication, and, up until then, even the most dependable dealers were not informed as to the names of cabinetmakers or the provenance of the items.

Early in my collecting, however, I had the good fortune to meet Charles Cornelius, the first curator of the American Wing of the Metropolitan Museum in New York. But the Museum itself was also new in the field. There followed Joseph Downs and Vincent Andrus as curators of the American Wing, and all of these were of great assistance to me.

I cannot remember when I was not interested in old things with a history. My maternal grandfather Colonel James Stinson's house in East Texas was filled with antebellum furniture long out of fashion, and at the Governor's Mansion in Austin I slept in Sam Houston's mahogany fourposter tester bed.

When I went off to boarding school I visited in New England many times and was doubtless exposed to early American furniture, but at the time it did not register. Later I traveled in England and began collecting English furniture. It is said that collecting is a disease. I think I had it from childhood. In Austin the streets were not paved and were covered with beautiful pebbles. When wet they sparkled like jewels, and in the spring the ditches on each side of the street were filled with a variety of wild flowers which could be pressed. These pebbles and flowers formed my first collection.

About 1920 my brother, Will, and I had an apartment in New York. One day I was in the studio of a friend, the great portrait painter, Wayman Adams. There he had an American country Queen Anne armchair which, for some strange reason, filled me with curiosity and excitement. When I heard it was American, the spell fell upon me—where could I go to find another one like it? I immediately began to search and the one now in the Maple Bedroom is that chair. Recently I had the good fortune to be able to buy the Adams' chair from his heir. Now I look at it and I cannot imagine why I was so excited over that simple chair.

When our idea was first conceived my brother, Will, and I had meant to collect only furniture, thinking whatever museum accepted it would regard it as a nucleus for other accessions in the decorative arts. It has been just the last comparatively few years, therefore, since I thought of giving Bayou Bend to the Museum of Fine Arts, that I attempted to collect paintings, metalwares and ceramics.

Bayou Bend, built in 1927 for my brothers, Will and Mike, and myself was never intended to be other than a home. However, the time came when it was filled with American furnishings and I was faced with the dilemma that there was not a museum in Texas fitted to house the collection. So, in 1956, after much hesitation I offered the house, gardens and holdings to the Museum of Fine Arts, Houston. The gift was accepted in 1958.

Of course, after I decided to give Bayou Bend as a museum, it was quite necessary to make many alterations in the rooms to fit the various periods of furniture. These and other steps necessary to convert the home to a house museum were completed in 1965 and Bayou Bend was opened to the public in early 1966. Later, extra space was utilized to create the Dorothy Chillman Empire Suite and recently the Belter Parlor.

While I shall always love Bayou Bend and everything there, in one sense I have always considered I was only holding my collection in trust for its transition. I had rather the Bayou Bend Collection not be called a museum. This seems to me too pretentious a term. I trust, however, the objects which are housed there have museum quality.

Texas, an empire in itself, geographically and historically, sometimes seems to be regarded as remote or alien to the rest of our nation. I hope in a modest way Bayou Bend may serve as a bridge to bring us closer to the heart of an American heritage which unites us.

August 1973

Acknowledgments

In 1965, when I became the first curator of Bayou Bend, I was determined to make the Collection available in published form. Now, nearly nine years later, this determination has become a reality.

Such an undertaking would not have been possible without the assistance and co-operation of many people. First, I should like to thank Miss Ima Hogg for having the vision to bring the Collection together and for her continued interest and support. Philippe de Montebello, Director of The Museum of Fine Arts, has supported this project from its inception. Dean Frederick Failey, Assistant Curator, has contributed enormously, not only in assembling and organizing great quantities of information pertaining to the Collection but also in reading the manuscript innumerable times and making invaluable suggestions. In addition, he has written the entire chapter on silver and four captions for paintings. Babette Fraser Warren has lent her professional ability in editing and proofreading the manuscript and in addition has given wifely encouragement and understanding throughout the project. A number of Bayou Bend Docents have contributed in many ways. Among those who ought to be singled out are Mrs. Edward Babcock, Mrs. Charles Robertson, Mrs. Wallace Shanks and Mrs. Newton Wray.

Staff members of other museums and institutions have been extremely helpful, especially Kathryn Buhler, Museum of Fine Arts, Boston; Benno Forman, The Henry Francis du Pont Winterthur Museum; Morrison Heckscher, Metropolitan Museum of Art, New York; Brock Jobe, Museum of Fine Arts, Boston; and J. Peter Spang, Historic Deerfield. Dealers, too, particularly Albert Sack, Bernard Levy and Robert Vose, have been generous with both time and information. Edward A. Bourdon and Allen Mewbourn took the photographs. Bert Clarke and Robert C. Lewis of The Press of A. Colish designed the book. The index was prepared by Kate S. Leader. One person, Mrs. Prim Specht, has worked devotedly with this book since the very beginning. She has transformed it through numerous drafts from illegibly scrawled yellow legal-sized sheets to finished manuscript. Her reliability, devotion and good humor have eased that monumental task. To her and all the other individuals who contributed to this book I am eternally grateful. The National Endowment for the Arts has made the book possible through a grant under their museum program. The Friends of Bayou Bend provided matching funds. To both I express heartfelt thanks.

DAVID B. WARREN

August 1973

Short Title Index

American Paintings, I, II
American Paintings in the Museum of Fine Arts, Boston, 2 vols. Boston, Museum of Fine Arts, 1969.

Baltimore Furniture
Baltimore Furniture: The Work of Baltimore and Annapolis Cabinetmakers from 1760-1810. Baltimore, Museum of Art, 1947.

Bayley
Frank W. Bayley. *Life and Works of John Singleton Copley.* Boston, 1915.

Belknap
Waldron Phoenix Belknap, Jr. *American Colonial Painting Materials for a History.* Cambridge, Mass., The Belknap Press of Harvard University Press, 1959.

Biddle
James Biddle. *American Art from American Collections.* New York, Metropolitan Museum of Art, 1963.

Bishop
Robert Bishop. *Centuries and Styles of the American Chair, 1640-1970.* New York, E. P. Dutton, 1972.

Bolton
Theodore E. Bolton. *Early American Portrait Draftsmen in Crayons.* New York, F. F. Sherman, 1923.

Buhler
Kathryn C. Buhler. *American Silver 1655-1825 in the Museum of Fine Arts, Boston,* 2 vols. Boston, Museum of Fine Arts, 1972.

Buhler and Hood
Kathryn C. Buhler and Graham Hood. *American Silver, Garvan and Other Collections, in the Yale University Art Gallery,* 2 vols. New Haven, Conn., Yale University Art Gallery, 1970.

Burton
E. Milby Burton. *Charleston Silver, 1690-1860.* The Charleston Museum, 1942.

Carpenter
Ralph E. Carpenter, Jr. *The Arts and Crafts of Newport, Rhode Island, 1640-1820.* Preservation Society of Newport County, 1954.

Clarke
Hermann Frederick Clarke and Henry Wilder Foote. *Jeremiah Dummer, Colonial Craftsman and Merchant, 1645-1718.* Boston, Houghton Mifflin Co., 1935.

Comstock
Helen Comstock. *American Furniture: Seventeenth, Eighteenth, and Nineteenth Century Styles.* New York, The Viking Press, 1962.

Comstock, "Drawings of John Singleton Copley"
Helen Comstock. "Drawings of John Singleton Copley," *Panorama, Harry Shaw Newman Gallery,* II. New York, Harry Shaw Newman, 1947.

Davidson
Marshall B. Davidson. *The American Heritage History of Colonial Antiques.* New York, American Heritage Publishing Co., Inc., 1967.

Downs
Joseph Downs. *American Furniture in the Henry Francis du Pont Winterthur Museum: Queen Anne and Chippendale Periods.* New York, Macmillan Co., 1952.

Downs, *Picture Book*
Joseph Downs. *American Chippendale Furniture: A Picture Book.* New York, Metropolitan Museum of Art, 1949.

Eastlake
Charles Eastlake. *Hints on Household Taste in Furniture Upholstery and Other Details.* London, Longmans Green and Company, 1878; reprinted, New York, Dover Publications, 1969.

Fales, *Essex County Furniture*
Dean A. Fales, Jr. *Essex County Furniture: Documented Treasures from Local Collections, 1660-1860.* Salem, The Essex Institute, 1965.

Fales, *Painted Furniture*
Dean A. Fales, Jr. *American Painted Furniture, 1660-1880.* New York, E. P. Dutton, 1972.

Fales, *Samuel McIntire*
Dean A. Fales, Jr. "The Furniture of McIntire," *Samuel McIntire, A Bicentennial Symposium, 1747-1957.* Salem, The Essex Institute, 1957.

Fales, *Early American Silver*
Martha Gandy Fales. *Early American Silver for the Cautious Collector.* New York, Funk and Wagnalls, 1970.

Fales, *Winterthur Museum*
Martha Gandy Fales. *American Silver in the Henry Francis du Pont Winterthur Museum.* The Henry Francis du Pont Winterthur Museum, 1958.

Flynt and Fales
Henry N. Flynt and Martha Gandy Fales. *The Heritage Foundation Collection of Silver: With Biographical Sketches of New England Silversmiths, 1625-1825*. Old Deerfield, Mass., The Heritage Foundation, 1968.

Foote
Henry Wilder Foote. *John Smibert, Painter*. Cambridge, Mass., Harvard University Press, 1950.

Forman
Benno Forman. "Urban Aspects of Massachusetts Furniture in the Late Seventeenth Century," *Country Cabinetwork and Simple City Furniture*. The Henry Francis du Pont Winterthur Museum, 1970.

Gardner and Feld
Albert Ten Eyck Gardner and Stuart P. Feld. *American Paintings: A Catalogue of the Collection of the Metropolitan Museum of Art, I, Painters Born by 1815*. New York, Metropolitan Museum of Art, 1965.

Gilbert Stuart
Gilbert Stuart, Portraitist of the Young Republic, 1755-1828. Providence, Museum of Art, The Rhode Island School of Design, 1967.

Halsey
R. T. Haines Halsey. *Catalogue of an Exhibition of Silver Used in New York, New Jersey, and the South*. New York, Metropolitan Museum of Art, 1911.

Hammerslough
Philip H. Hammerslough. *American Silver*, 3 vols. and supplement. Hartford, Conn., privately printed, 1958, 1960, 1965.

Hanks
David Hanks. *American Art of the Colonies and Early Republic*. Chicago, The Art Institute of Chicago, 1971.

Hipkiss
Edwin J. Hipkiss. *The M. and M. Karolik Collection of Eighteenth Century American Arts*. Museum of Fine Arts, Cambridge, Mass., Harvard University Press, 1941.

Hood
Graham Hood. *American Silver: A History of Style, 1650-1900*. New York, Praeger Publishers, 1971.

Hornor
William Macpherson Hornor, Jr. *The Blue Book, Philadelphia Furniture, William Penn to George Washington*. Philadelphia, privately printed, 1935.

Kane
Patricia E. Kane. "The Joiners of Seventeenth Century Hartford County," *The Connecticut Historical Society Bulletin*, Vol. 35, July 1970.

Kimball
Fiske Kimball. *Domestic Architecture of the American Colonies and of the Early Republic*. New York, Charles Scribner's Sons, 1922; reprinted, New York, Dover Publications, 1966.

Kirk, *American Chairs*
John T. Kirk. *American Chairs: Queen Anne and Chippendale*. New York, Alfred A. Knopf, 1972.

Kirk, *Connecticut Furniture*
John T. Kirk. *Connecticut Furniture: Seventeenth and Eighteenth Centuries*. Hartford, The Wadsworth Atheneum, 1967.

Kirk, *Early American Furniture*
John T. Kirk. *Early American Furniture*. New York, Alfred A. Knopf, 1970.

Lea
Zilla Rider Lea, ed. *The Ornamented Chair*. Rutland, Vermont, Charles E. Tuttle Company, 1960.

Lockwood
Luke Vincent Lockwood. *Colonial Furniture in America*, 2 vols. New York, Charles Scribner's Sons, 1926, 3rd edition.

Lockwood, *Pendleton Collection*
Luke Vincent Lockwood. *The Pendleton Collection*. Providence, The Rhode Island School of Design, 1904.

Lyndhurst
Catalogue of the Valuable Library of the Rt. Hon. Lord Lyndhurst, Deceased: also a few engravings and sketches by J. S. Copley, R. A. London, Christie, Manson and Woods, 1864.

Lyon
Irving W. Lyon. *The Colonial Furniture of New England*. Boston, Houghton Mifflin, 1891.

McClelland
Nancy McClelland. *Duncan Phyfe and the English Regency, 1795-1830*. New York, Scott, 1939.

Middleton
Margaret Simons Middleton. *Jeremiah Theus, Colonial Artist of Charles Town*. Columbia, University of South Carolina Press, 1953.

Miller
V. Isabelle Miller. *Furniture by New York Cabinetmakers, 1650 to 1860*. New York, Museum of the City of New York, 1956.

Miller, *New York Silversmiths*
V. Isabelle Miller. *New York Silversmiths of the Seventeenth Century*. New York, Museum of the City of New York, 1963.

Montgomery
Charles F. Montgomery. *American Furniture in the Henry Francis du Pont Winterthur Museum: The Federal Period*. New York, The Viking Press, 1966.

Nineteenth Century America
Berry B. Tracy, Marilynn Johnson, Marvin Schwartz and Suzanne Boorsch. *Nineteenth-Century America: Furniture and Other Decorative Arts.* New York, Metropolitan Museum of Art, 1970.

Notebook
The Notebook of John Smibert. Boston, The Massachusetts Historical Society, 1969.

Nutting
Wallace Nutting. *Furniture Treasury.* Framingham, Mass., Old America Company, 1928-1933; reprinted, New York, Macmillan Co., 1948, 1954.

Parker and Wheeler
Barbara Neville Parker and Anna Bolling Wheeler. *John Singleton Copley: American Portraits in Oil, Pastel and Miniature with Biographical Sketches.* Boston, Museum of Fine Arts, 1938.

Perkins
A. T. Perkins. *Sketch of the Life and List of some of the Works of John Singleton Copley.* Boston, 1873.

Phillips
John Marshall Phillips. *Masterpieces of New England Silver, 1650-1800.* New Haven, Gallery of Fine Arts, Yale University, 1939.

Pinckney
Pauline A. Pinckney. *Painting in Texas.* Austin, The University of Texas Press, 1967.

Prime
Phoebe Prime. *Philadelphia Silver, 1682-1800.* The Philadelphia Museum of Art, 1956.

Prown, I, II
Jules David Prown. *John Singleton Copley,* 2 vols. Cambridge, Mass., Harvard University Press, 1966.

Randall
Richard H. Randall, Jr. *American Furniture in the Museum of Fine Arts, Boston.* Boston, Museum of Fine Arts, 1965.

Randall, *New Hampshire*
Richard H. Randall, Jr. *The Decorative Arts of New Hampshire, 1725-1825.* Manchester, N. H., The Currier Gallery of Art, 1964.

Rhode Island Furniture
The John Brown House Loan Exhibition of Rhode Island Furniture. Providence, The Rhode Island Historical Society, 1965.

Rice
Norman S. Rice. *New York Furniture before 1840.* Albany, Albany Institute of History and Art, 1962.

Rosenbaum
Jeanette W. Rosenbaum, *Myer Myers, Goldsmith, 1723-1795.* Philadelphia, Jewish Publication Society of America, 1954.

Sack
Albert Sack. *Fine Points of Furniture: Early American.* New York, Crown Publishers, 1950.

Sack, *Opportunities*
Israel Sack, Inc. *Opportunities in American Antiques,* brochures. New York, 1956-1973.

Schiffer
Margaret Berwind Schiffer. *Furniture and Its Makers of Chester County, Pennsylvania.* Philadelphia, University of Pennsylvania Press, 1966.

Schwartz
Marvin D. Schwartz. *American Interiors, 1675-1885: A Guide to the American Period Rooms in the Brooklyn Museum.* The Brooklyn Museum, 1968.

Sellars
Charles Coleman Sellars. *Charles Willson Peale.* New York, Charles Scribner's Sons, 1969.

XVII & XVIII Century American Furniture and Paintings
XVII & XVIII Century American Furniture and Paintings, The Celebrated Collection Formed by the Late Mr. & Mrs. Luke Vincent Lockwood. New York, Parke-Bernet Galleries, May 1954.

Smith
George Smith. *A Collection of Designs for Household Furniture and Interior Decoration.* London, J. Taylor, 1808.

Special Loan Exhibits
Special Loan Exhibits from Private Collections 1964, 1965, 1966. Delaware Antiques Show Catalogue, n.d.

Stoneman
Vernon C. Stoneman. *John & Thomas Seymour: Cabinetmakers in Boston, 1794-1816.* Boston, Special Publications, 1965.

Stoneman, *Supplement*
Vernon C. Stoneman. *A Supplement to John and Thomas Seymour: Cabinetmakers in Boston, 1794-1816.* Boston, Special Publications, 1965.

"The Prentis Collection"
"The Prentis Collection," *Historical New Hampshire,* Vol. 14, December 1958.

Tracy
Berry B. Tracy. "The Decorative Arts," *Classical America, 1815-1845.* Newark, New Jersey, The Newark Museum, 1963.

Warren

David B. Warren. *Southern Silver: An Exhibition of Silver Made in the South Prior to 1860.* Houston, The Museum of Fine Arts, 1968.

Webster

Thomas Webster. *An Encyclopaedia of Domestic Economy.* . . . New York, D. Meridith Reese, 1845.

Welsh

Peter C. Welsh. *American Folk Art: The Art and Spirit of a People from the Eleanor and Mabel Van Alstyne Collection.* Washington, D.C., Smithsonian Institution, 1965.

Winchester

Alice Winchester, ed. *The Antiques Treasury.* New York, E. P. Dutton, 1959.

Photography Credits

Edward Bourdon

2, 3, 4, 6, 7, 8, 9, 10, 11, 13, 14, 18, 19, 20, 21, 22, 24, 25, 26, 30, 35, 37, 38, 39, 40, 41, 43, 44, 45, 47, 48, 51, 53, 56, 57, 58, 60, 63, 64, 65, 66, 69, 71, 72, 84, 85, 91, 94, 95, 99, 103, 105, 106, 107, 108, 109, 110, 112, 113, 116, 117, 118, 122, 124, 127, 132, 134, 147, 151, 153, 161, 166, 178, 179, 180, 181, 182, 183, 185, 188, 189, 190, 192, 193, 194, 195, 197, 200, 201, 202, 203, 204, 206, 207, 211, 212, 213, 216, 217, 218, 220, 221, 222, 223, 225, 232, 257, 269, 273, 278-343, 346-355

F. Wilbur Seiders

27, 104

Allen Mewbourn

Color plates, room views, 1, 5, 12, 15, 16, 17, 23, 28, 29, 31, 32, 33, 36, 42, 46, 49, 50, 52, 54, 55, 59, 61, 62, 67, 68, 70, 73, 74, 75, 76, 77, 78, 79, 80, 81, 82, 82, 86, 86, 88, 89, 92, 93, 96, 97, 98, 100, 101, 102, 111, 114, 115, 119, 120, 121, 123, 126, 128, 129, 130, 131, 133, 135, 136, 137, 138, 139, 140, 141, 142, 143, 144, 145, 146, 148, 149, 150, 152, 154, 155, 156, 157, 158, 159, 160, 162, 164, 165, 167, 168, 169, 170, 171, 172, 173, 174, 175, 176, 177, 184, 186, 187, 191, 198, 199, 205, 208, 209, 210, 214, 215, 224, 226, 227, 228, 229, 230, 231, 233, 234-256, 258-268, 270-272, 274-277, 287 (mark), 306 (mark), 311 (mark), 314 (mark), 316 (mark), 340 (mark), 344, 345

Introduction

When Miss Hogg purchased her first American antique in 1920 with the intention of collecting for a Texas museum, she wanted to make available to the citizens of her beloved State the rich colonial heritage of their nation, a heritage not native geographically to that area. Her brother, William C. Hogg, shared her interest and worked toward that goal until his death in 1930. A number of important pieces found today at Bayou Bend were acquired during that early period. Through the ensuing years the collection increased and by the 1950's had assumed its present form and considerable size. It became apparent that in carrying out her plan — to give the collection to a museum — Miss Hogg would have been required to provide a structure in which to house it. She decided, therefore, to leave the collection in her home. Her collection of early American art was accepted by the Museum of Fine Arts in 1958. A complicated program of conversion from private home to house museum followed, and by early 1966 the Bayou Bend Collection was opened to the public; since then it has been seen by more than 200,000 visitors. The Collection is the only such gathering of Americana in the Southwestern United States. As Miss Hogg intended, it is, accordingly, a vital cultural resource for many people to whom examples of the art and craftsmanship of their forebears would not be accessible.

In addition, the Collection serves as the basis for a survey course in American Art at Rice University and provides a program which augments courses in American history taught within the Houston school system.

It has been long felt, however, that the Americana at Bayou Bend should be even more widely available. A great collector once noted: "Because books have been helpful to me in my collecting I wanted to make my collection available to others through them. This seemed especially important since many collectors might never get [to my museum] and besides one needs books for study in his home."[1] These words perfectly describe the need for this volume, conceived as a further extension of Miss Hogg's original purpose. Also, in anticipation of a heightened interest in America's past during the approaching Bicentennial year, it is appropriate for such a book to appear at this time. Happily, its publication also coincides with the fiftieth anniversary of the Museum of Fine Arts, Houston.

Approach

This book has been conceived with a dual purpose. First, it provides the casual reader with a survey of the Collection as it now appears in room settings. Second, for the more avid reader, attention has been focused on the three major aspects of the Collection — furniture, painting and silver. In the first section, short explanatory essays place the furniture in its stylistic context. Detailed analyses of individual examples follow. The paintings and silver have received similar treatment. Limitations of time and space have made it necessary to omit whole segments of the Collection, such as pewter, ceramics and glass. Likewise, it has not been possible to consider every example of furniture or painting, although the entire collection of American silver is represented.

Because of the inevitable difficulty of arranging the diverse material in a book of this nature, many authors have resorted to an alphabetical listing, often with confusing results. Here the furniture has been divided as to period and considered in sequence from the simplest seating forms, to tables, case pieces and miscellaneous forms, all arranged by provenance from North to South. Traditional furniture and art have been placed in a separate section. The paintings are arranged chronologically according to the birth date of the artist. Silver is grouped by form, beginning with drinking vessels, and is discussed chronologically within each grouping. Biographical information on painters and craftsmen has not been included except in the case of several relatively unknown men. Measurements record overall dimensions. Secondary woods, with a few exceptions, have been identified visually.

D.B.W.

1. Montgomery, p. 6.

xvi

The Bayou Bend Collection

THE PINE ROOM. About 1700 wooden paneling was introduced to American interiors. Fielded panels, pilasters and molding around the fireplace opening are typical of the first half of the eighteenth century. Woodwork in this room is based on that of the Metcalf Bowler House built in Portsmouth, Rhode Island.[1] Following usage of the early eighteenth century, the fireplace opening is lined with Dutch delft tiles circa 1690–1720. All the furniture in the room was made in New England. At the left of the fireplace is an eighteenth century English brass kettle and stand, and the brass chandelier is also English. Over the fireplace are mezzotint portraits of William and Mary, the monarchs whose names have been given to American furniture made between 1690 and 1725.

1. That room is now a museum installation at the Metropolitan Museum, New York (*The Metropolitan Museum of Art Guide to the Collections: The American Wing*, 1961, p. 18).

The Seventeenth Century Period 1640-1695
The William and Mary Period 1695-1725

During the reign of Elizabeth I (1558–1603) a vigorous native style of furniture emerged. It was a mixture of English vernacular medieval traditions combined with Italianate and Flemish Renaissance detail. These foreign influences came from the Low Countries and were transferred primarily by immigrant craftsmen. However, two design books by Hans Vredeman de Vries, *Architectura* (1577) and *Differents Portraicts de Menuiserie* (1588), as well as several other foreign publications, also brought the Flemish Renaissance to English shores. The massive furniture of this style was made in a simple fashion by men called joiners, using pegged, mortise and tenon construction. Often it was covered with a wealth of ornament: inlays, shallow carving, bulbous turnings. This profusion of detail reflected the ebullient confidence of the Elizabethan era, paralleling the phenomenon of the elaborate "prodigy houses" built at the same time.

Although the traditions of the Elizabethan period continued during the early Stuart era of James I (1603–1625) and Charles I (1625–1649), furniture became somewhat lighter in proportion. In decoration, bulbous turnings were replaced by more delicate baluster or bobbin shapes, and applied surface ornament, such as split balusters, bosses and geometric panels, was introduced.

When the English settlers colonized the Atlantic seaboard in the seventeenth century, they brought with them the ideas, tastes and fashions of the late Elizabethan and early Jacobean eras. American furniture made before the 1690's reflected the traditional Elizabethan-Jacobean joined style. Construction techniques were simple and apparent. Ornament was derived primarily from turned members. However, shallow carved decoration, strapwork, meandering vines, flowers, rosettes and, occasionally, inlay appeared on case pieces (No. 31) but, generally, was restricted to the frontal surfaces. Later, geometric panels, turned split-balusters and bosses were applied (Nos. 32 & 34). Paint was also used to give the suggestion of rich, expensive materials (No. 27).

As in Elizabethan England, the variety of furniture forms was limited, even in the wealthiest households. Joined stools and benches were the most prevalent seating form, and chairs, both those with framed panels, called wainscot, and those with turned members (Nos. 1 & 5), were less numerous. Case pieces included utilitarian paneled chests, often with one or more drawers (No. 31), and both court and press cupboards. Tables were either the trestle or framed variety.

The 1690's saw one of the most sweeping changes in the history of American furniture take hold, as presaged by revolutionary events in English cabinetmaking during the last half of the seventeenth century. At that time, the rise of a radically new style was accompanied by the introduction of major innovations in construction. The new style reflected developments in England that had begun with the restoration of the monarchy in 1660. During the years of exile on the continent, Charles II (1660–1685) and his courtiers became conversant with late mannerist, early baroque, French and Dutch fashions. After the court's return from Holland and France, these continental influences sharply altered English taste. The traditional heavy oak style and additive medieval ornament were succeeded by luxurious, light, elegant walnut furniture of attenuated proportions and unified compositions following Renaissance principles.

This shift toward more delicate expression brought with it the necessity for construction techniques of an equivalent sophistication. Thus, for the first time, English furniture began to be made by cabinetmakers using dovetails and board construction, rather than by joiners using the framed mortise and tenon construction which had been traditional since the middle ages. Richly figured veneers and marquetry, in the Dutch taste, were extensively applied to case furniture. Lavishly upholstered furniture was also made.

Additional foreign influences were exerted upon English taste following the 1662 marriage of Charles II to Catherine of Braganza, a Portuguese princess. Catherine and her entourage introduced products that had come to Portugal from the Orient, notably tea, porcelain, caning and lacquer. Portuguese furniture with baroque scrolls and feet of a paintbrush shape was also introduced at this time.

The Dutch influences in England received further impetus when William of Orange and his wife Mary Stuart ascended the throne in 1688, bringing with them both Dutch fashions and Dutch craftsmen. The names of those monarchs have been given to the early baroque style in America.

The William and Mary style, which began to appear in Boston during the 1690's, dominated American taste during the first quarter of the eighteenth century. As in England, heavy forms of the earlier period gave way to taller, more attenuated ones. Often the upper section of furniture was accented by ornament. Turned ball feet and carved paintbrush or Portuguese feet were used concurrently (Nos. 8, 13). Walnut, and occasionally maple, succeeded oak as the fashionable wood. However, paint also was used frequently to suggest rich exotic surfaces, such as ebony or cedar (Nos. 9, 15); and in some cases, painted imitation lacquer, called japanning, was also employed.

During this time a greater variety of furniture, including many new forms, was produced. Chairs continued to be of turned construction, but carved scrolled and leafy crests were introduced. Following continental practices, smaller, more intimate, round or oval drop-leaf dining tables (No. 24) replaced the rectangular form. Tables, too, were made with turned members. Case furniture was now fabricated by cabinetmakers using boarded construction and dovetailing, new construction techniques which permitted lighter, more refined work. Chests were raised up on turned legs of trumpet shape and usually veneered with figured woods carefully chosen for pattern (No. 33). Brass hardware, newly introduced, added to the surface ornament. New forms included the easy chair, couch, desk, dressing table and high chest.

THE MURPHY ROOM.   Paneling reproduced from that of a circa 1730 Connecticut house forms the setting for New England seventeenth century and William and Mary furniture.[2] The black and white painted oak floor, not unlike those seen in American seventeenth century portraits, is based on the treatment in a Hopkinton, New Hampshire, house. Late seventeenth and early eighteenth century delft wares, together with English and American pewter, are set on the table and in the cupboards. At the window are blue and white English crewel hangings made about 1700. The room is named for Katharine Prentis Murphy (1884–1967), the noted collector, who was a close friend of Miss Hogg.

2. The original room is now a museum installation at the New Hampshire Historical Society, Concord, a gift of Katharine Prentis Murphy ("The Prentis Collection," p. 13).

1   Great Chair   B.60.32

Connecticut, probably Norwich, 1670–1700
Ash. H.49 W.27½ D.21

This large slat-back chair is one of several nearly identical examples.[3] Particularly distinctive are the outsized mushroom-shaped terminals of the front posts, the ogee profile at the outer edge of each slat and the tall ovoid finials with delicate ring and ball turnings above. The juncture of the arms with the stiles has been altered in this example from a spot level with the middle slat to the present location, thus partially disguising a sharp rake seen on the arms of the other chairs. The bottoms of the legs, which have suffered through the years, originally terminated in rounded ball-like feet. Vase turnings on the stiles recall No. 5. One of the related examples has a history of Lebanon, Connecticut, ownership, and it is likely that these chairs were made in the Norwich area.

    3. Lyon, p. 144; Nutting, No. 1887 (he states that two other armchairs and a side chair are known); Winterthur (Bishop, No. 30); the Leffingwell Inn, Norwich, Connecticut (*Antiques*, June 1961, p. 568); a related but later armchair is in the Brooklyn Museum (Schwartz, frontispiece); *Antiques*, May 1970, p. 659.

2   Great Chair   B.69.520

New England, probably Massachusetts, 1670–1700
Oak. H.44¾ W.22 D.17⅝

Considerably smaller than the preceding example, this great chair is plain except for the flattened ball, ring and ball finials of the stiles and ball terminals of the front posts. The straight slats with concave upper corners are seen on a number of New England examples which usually have flat slat-like arms.[4] In this case, however, the turned arms appear to be correct.

    4. Comstock, No. 33; Bishop, No. 31.

3   Child's Chair   B.68.18

New England, probably Connecticut, 1710–1800
Maple. H.29⅝ W.15 D.12

Chairs made for children were not common in seventeenth century America. This one follows the lines of full-sized examples. Its inverted baluster finials and front post terminals together with light proportions suggest, however, a somewhat later date.

4   Armchair   B.69.40

Connecticut, 1710–1740
Maple. H.46¾ W.23 D.20½

Slat-back chairs continued to be popular into the eighteenth century. However, they were lighter and more vertical
than the earlier examples and often incorporated such William
and Mary features as boldly turned stretchers. The bulb turnings on the stiles, the shape of the arms, notched below, and
the pair of ringed stretchers are typical of a group of Connecticut chairs.[5]

5. Kirk, *Connecticut Furniture*, No. 192; Randall, No. 123.

5   Great Chair   B.69.354

East Haven-Branford, Connecticut, 1660–1700
Ash. H.49 W.26 D.19½

Repetition of elongated ogee shapes has been associated
with chairs originating in the New Haven Colony.[6] Here that
motif appears on the stiles and on the front posts. The baluster
spindles assume a similar shape. All of these features are seen in
another example with an East Haven–Branford provenance,
which was probably made by the same man.[7] The great chair
here has a history of ownership in the Harrison family of Branford. The arms of this piece, with their ogee turnings, are more
elaborate than the typical New England chair.

6. Patricia E. Kane, *Furniture of the New Haven Colony: The Seventeenth
Century Style*, The New Haven Colony Historical Society, 1973, p. 8.
7. Kane, *New Haven Colony*, p. 71; related examples, pp. 75–77; also
Kirk, *Connecticut Furniture*, No. 201. The Bayou Bend example is illustrated and discussed (Kane, p. 73).

6   Great Chair   B.56.4

Plymouth County, Massachusetts, 1660–1700
Oak, maple. H.43½ W.23¼ D.16

This type of chair, with turned spindles in the back, bears
the generic name "Carver," after a similar one owned by
Governor John Carver (1575–1621) of the Plymouth colony.
Although the double flattened ball of the front post terminals
and triple spindles with ball turnings are unusual in design,
nearly identical spindles appear on the Governor Carver example.[8] This chair has a history of ownership by the Ellis family
in Carver, Plymouth County.

8. Now at Pilgrim Hall, Plymouth. Similar spindles appear on a
"semi-Brewster" chair (Nutting, No. 1823).

7   Great Chair   B.69.350

Probably Massachusetts, 1680–1710
Maple. H. 46 W. 24½ D. 17½

Use of maple rather than ash or oak suggests that this chair was made later in the period. Remnants of red paint remind the twentieth century viewer that many of these early chairs were not originally finished in natural wood. The upper rail and one of the spindles are replacements.

8   Armchair   B.69.54

Massachusetts, 1700–1725
Maple. H. 47¾ W. 24 D. 19

The ubiquitous leaf and c-scroll carving of New England banister-back chairs is supplanted here by a more solid crest and scrolled beveled molding. This arched outline with projecting rectangle is similar to the shape of upholstered chairs.[9] The vase turnings on the front legs and stiles are shorter than usual. This chair and a matching side chair also at Bayou Bend have a history of ownership by John Bigelow (1674–1769) and his wife Jerusa Garfield Bigelow (1677–1758), natives of Watertown, Massachusetts, who in 1696 settled in nearby Marlboro, Massachusetts.

9. Comstock, No. 43.

9   Side Chair   B.66.14.2

Massachusetts, 1700–1725
Maple. H. 47¾ W. 19 D. 14¾

This side chair, one of two similar but not identical in the Collection, relates to the preceding armchair in its crest design. Unusual, however, is the bold arched, scrolled stretcher which echoes the lines above and unites the composition.[10]

10. This chair follows the design of a simpler English Restoration type ornamented with so-called Portuguese arches (Gertrude Z. Thomas, *Richer Than Spices*, New York, Alfred A. Knopf, 1965, p. 66).

10   Armchair   B.69.44
New England, 1700–1725
Maple. H.49 W.25 D.22¾

This five-banister-back armchair with c-scroll and foliate crest represents a form that with minor variations was made throughout New England. The flat banisters, which repeat the turned profile of the stiles, were a substitute for the more expensive and exotic caning (No. 14).

11   Side Chair   B.69.46
New England, 1700–1725
Maple. H.47½ W.19 D.16½

The four-banister-back side chair, made to match armchairs like No. 12, found similar popularity throughout New England.[11] Frequently, as here, chairs were painted black to suggest ebony.

11. Randall, No. 124.

12   Armchair   B.69.521
New England, 1700–1725
Maple. H.27⅞ W.24⅛ D.17

Shaped and flared arms often were embellished with scrolled terminals; simple turned feet were an alternative to the carved Portuguese variety (No. 10).

13   Armchair   B.58.106
      New England, 1700–1725
      Maple. H. 50½ W. 24¾ D. 22

      Although this chair is similar to No. 10, it varies in sev-
eral important details. Reeded slats fill the back, and an extra
medial stretcher extends between the side stretchers, which are
distinctively turned at the juncture. Although reeded slats appear frequently on Connecticut chairs, one example, thought
to be from New Hampshire or Massachusetts, has similar slats.[12]
Another, from New York, has a similar stretcher arrangement
and ball turnings.[13] As a result, specific attribution of provenance is difficult.

      12. Randall, *New Hampshire*, No. 3.
      13. Miller, No. 19.

14   Armchair   B.58.142
      England, 1690–1705
      Beech. H. 48¾ W. 26½ D. 24

      This cane-back chair represents the sort of fine imported
furniture that appeared in early eighteenth century Boston. Use
of beech, the bulb stretcher without a ring and the plain con-
figuration of the other stretchers indicate an English origin. In
terms of design, the crest, which extends over the stiles, is a later
feature stylistically than the treatment of the preceding examples. A brass plaque affixed to the back lists a series of eminent
Boston owners.[14]

      14. Judge Jonathan Remington (1677–1745); Judge Edmund Trow-
bridge (1700–1793); Judge Francis Dana (1743–1814); Richard Henry
Dana (1787–1870). The chair descended in the Dana family.

15   Armchair   B.61.40
      Boston, 1715–1725
      Maple. H. 46 W. 24½ D. 24

      The final development of William and Mary chairs in-
corporated molded stiles that continue into a crest. The treatment anticipates the Queen Anne design. This chair belongs to
a body of related arm and side chairs made in Boston, all of
which feature small carved leaves at the crest and turned rear
legs. A punched double E on the rear seat rail of this example
appears on another related chair that descended in the Edes
family of Boston.[15] This piece probably has the same provenance. It is grained to resemble cedar.

      15. Randall, No. 127. A side chair which seems to be identical to the
Bayou Bend example is in Pilgrim Hall, Plymouth; a slightly later but
related armchair is in the Vassall-Longfellow House, Cambridge; a
similar side chair is at the Henry Ford Museum, Dearborn (Comstock,
No. 37). All four feet of the Bayou Bend chair have been cut out in the
center and later pieced, indicating that at one point it was converted
into a rocker.

16   Couch   B.69.355

England, 1690–1715
Beech. H. 41⅞ W. 20¾ L. 60

The couch, a new form introduced in England during
the Restoration, became fashionable in the colonies at the turn
of the eighteenth century. As originally conceived, couches
were made to match sets of chairs, and the design of back and
legs is very similar. This particular example, made of beech and
painted black, is caned on the back and bottom. Although it
has a long history of ownership in Ipswich, Massachusetts, use
of beech throughout and turned bulb stretchers without rings
indicate an English origin.[16]

16. This couch was incorrectly published as being of Pennsylvania
origin (Comstock, No. 89). A related beech daybed, also probably
English, is in the Museum of Fine Arts, Boston (Randall, No. 188). The
feet of the Bayou Bend example have been restored.

17   Easy Chair   B.58.104

Massachusetts, probably Ipswich, 1715–1730
Maple. H. 48⅜ W. 39⅝ D. 33

Upholstered chairs with wings and large horizontally
rolled arms were an innovation in the William and Mary
period. The design of these easy chairs, as they were called in
the eighteenth century, afforded the occupant both comfort
and protection against drafts. Well-developed Portuguese feet,
scalloped skirt and simple arched crest indicate that this example was made toward the latter half of the period. This chair
was traditionally owned by the Parsons family of Ipswich and
is thought to have been made there.[17]

17. This chair has been illustrated without upholstery (Sack, p. 64).

18   Stool   B.58.105

New England, 1700–1725
Maple. H. 21½ W. 21⅜ D. 13¼

Small joined stools were the most common seating form
during the seventeenth and early eighteenth centuries. Light
proportions, slender vase and ring turnings and the use of
maple suggest this to be a late example of the form.

19   Stand   B.69.14

New England, 1700–1725
Maple. H.26¼ W.27 D.18

This type of stand evolved from the joint stool, an earlier form which often served the dual function of table and seat. The combination of flattened ball and double vase turning is unusual.

20   Stand   B.61.95

New England, 1700–1725
Maple, pine. H.28 W.29¾ D.21

Surviving examples of the small utilitarian trestle-base stand or table are rare. Unusual details on this example are the oval top and turning on both stretchers.[18]

18. This piece is illustrated (Nutting, No. 1204); a gateleg table with related, although not identical, turnings is in the Museum of Fine Arts, Boston (Randall, No. 73).

21   Table   B.58.145

New England, 1690–1715
Maple, pine. H.38⅞ W.43 D.27¼

The rectangular stretcher form, today dubbed "tavern table," undoubtedly found use in both public and private settings. This example has especially fine turnings. The high placement of the front and rear stretchers is an uncommon arrangement.[19]

19. For related examples, see Sack, p. 236; Nutting, No. 854.

22 Table

B.22.18

New England, Connecticut?, 1690–1725
Oak. H. 27½ W. 46½ D. 27

Tall vase-turned legs and sausage-turned stretchers suggest a later date than would be expected for an oak table, the drawer of which is hung on side runners. The shaping of the skirt is an especially unusual feature.[20]

20. For related examples, see Nutting, No. 852; Lockwood, No. 697.

23 Table

B.69.351

New Hampshire, 1710–1730
Maple, pine. H. 25½ W. 36⅝ D. 26½

This splay-legged table is closely related to several others.[21] Like them, it is distinguished by turned, sharply raked legs, imaginatively cut-out skirts (here rather like a high chest) and, in most cases, well-developed Portuguese feet. Minor differences suggest that these tables were not made in the same shop but probably originated in the same locale. Traces of red paint reveal its original finish.

21. Nutting, No. 1225; Randall, *New Hampshire*, No. 2; Winchester, p. 14; "The Prentis Collection," Fig. 8. All of these tables have oval tops. Although a rectangular top appears on another somewhat different example at Shelburne Museum, Vermont (Winchester, p. 286), it is likely that the top of the Bayou Bend example is a replacement.

24 Gateleg Table

B.59.71

New England, possibly Rhode Island, 1700–1725
Walnut, maple, chestnut. H. 28 W. 48½ L. 56¾ (open)

Paired vases, ring turnings and finely carved Portuguese feet lend distinction to this large gateleg table.[22] Although maple was the more usual primary material, on occasion walnut was employed. Use of chestnut suggests a possible Rhode Island provenance.

22. Only a few examples with Portuguese feet are known (Nutting, No. 963); one at Winterthur (*Antiques*, January 1957, p. 59); one at Historic Deerfield (*Antiques*, September 1956, p. 232); one at Colonial Williamsburg.

25 Gateleg Table

B.71.8

Pennsylvania or Virginia, 1710–1725
Walnut, pine. H. 28⅞ W. 42⅛ L. 51⅞ (open)

At about the turn of the eighteenth century, the oval drop-leaf gateleg table succeeded the rectangular form. Crisply turned legs with tall vase shapes suggest that this example was made in Pennsylvania or possibly Virginia.[23]

23. For related examples, see Sack, p. 240; Schiffer, No. 120.

26 Butterfly Table

B.69.51

Connecticut, 1700–1735
Cherry. H. 27½ W. 41 (open) D. 34

While swinging bracket supports are not unknown in European drop-leaf tables, the wing shape used in "butterfly" tables is so distinctive that the resulting form is purely American. Although these tables were made throughout New England, they seem to have been especially popular in Connecticut. Surprisingly, however, few of these are made of cherry, a wood normally associated with that state.

27 Toilet Table

B.70.24

Northeastern Massachusetts, 1690–1710
Oak, pine. H. 32¾ W. 27⁵⁄₁₆ D. 19
Gift of the Houston Chapter, Kappa Alpha Theta

This toilet table is one of a painted group made in Northeastern Massachusetts. In its original state the legs, stretchers and grooved moldings were painted black, the moldings, panels and drawer front, red. Traces remain of the delicate asymmetrical trees which ornamented the panels of the chest section. The drawer front was originally paneled, dividing it into two smaller sections. Two other surviving tables have the same bobbin turnings,[24] while the remaining related pieces stand on the more conventional vase and ring-turned legs.[25] The pine lid is fitted with its original cleat hinge. Although the original use of the form is not certain, it probably served as an early dressing or toilet table.

24. Nutting, No. 213, and Lockwood, No. 236, now in the Henry Ford Museum, Dearborn. This latter example is, however, made of maple.
25. The Brooklyn Museum (Comstock, No. 58); the Shelburne Museum, Vermont (*Antiques*, May 1947, p. 442); Winterthur (Forman, Fig. 7); The New York Historical Society; Nutting, Nos. 214–216. The painted ornament of these toilet tables relates to a group of one-drawer chests (Comstock, No. 66; Nutting, No. 53).

28   Dressing Table   B.69.52

Boston, 1695–1710
Walnut, pine. H.28½ W.38 D.22

Dressing tables with one drawer, the earliest type, are far less common today than the three-drawer variety. This example is finished in solid walnut, rather than the more usual veneers. The turned legs, distinctive in their high rounded cup with little rebate below, are seen on another dressing table, a high chest and a slate-top table, probably made in Massachusetts.[26] The elongate vase turnings at the top and bottom of the legs appear on a later dressing table now at Winterthur. It has a Boston provenance.[27] The Bayou Bend example also has a Boston family history.

26. Nutting, Nos. 388, 1092; Randall, No. 55.
27. Winterthur, Acc. No. 58.584.

29   Dressing Table   B.69.45

Boston, 1700–1725
Walnut, pine. H.31½ W.34 D.21¾

This three-drawer dressing table with arched skirt is the final fully developed William and Mary form. Figured walnut veneers have been used here — four flitches fitted together on the top, surrounded by inlaid herringbone and crossbanded borders. Similar veneers grace the drawer fronts. A thin applied beading emphasizes the vigorous line of the skirt. In profile, the cup-turned legs, virtually identical to others known to have been turned in Boston, are the same as those on a Boston high chest at Winterthur.[28] This dressing table was, according to tradition, owned by Parson Thomas Smith, who lived in Newport, Rhode Island, and later Falmouth, now Portland, Maine.

28. Forman, p. 21.

30   Miniature Chest   B.57.92

Robert Crosman, 1707–1799
Taunton, Massachusetts, ca. 1727
Pine. H.20¼ W.22¾ D.13

Simple plank construction was used in making this one-drawer chest. The front and drawer below are embellished with thin spreading trees of life, a type of ornament identified as the product of Robert Crosman of Taunton, Massachusetts.[29] The general simplicity of the ornament and the date 1727 painted on the back indicate that this example is early in Crosman's *oeuvre*.[30]

29. *Antiques*, April 1933, pp. 135–138.
30. There are two other similar examples (Lockwood, Fig. 39; Comstock, No. 180).

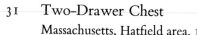

31   **Two-Drawer Chest**   B.69.356

Massachusetts, Hatfield area, 1670–1710
Oak, pine. H. 39 W. 49½ D. 18¼

The seventeenth century's fondness for ornament is no-where better expressed than on this richly carved chest. This design, with vine, tulip and leaf motifs, appears on examples made in the Connecticut River Valley around Hadley and Hat-field, Massachusetts, and possibly as far south as Hartford, Con-necticut.[31] Motifs in the panels — lozenges with initials, rosette tulips and vines — and undulating vines on the stiles place this chest stylistically into the Hatfield group.[32] The back side of the bottom drawer bears the inscription *Mary Allyns Chistt Cutte and joyned by Nich: Disbrowe*. Although once thought fully to document this chest, evidence points to the fact that the inscription is spurious.[33]

31. Kirk, *Connecticut Furniture*, No. 21.
32. Kane, p. 68.
33. *Antiques*, May 1933, p. 171, reveals that Disbrowe did not know how to write. He worked in Hartford, but this chest is a Hatfield type.

32   **Two-Drawer Chest**   B.69.353

Possibly Peter Blin, 1639/40–1725
Wethersfield, Connecticut, 1670–1710
Oak, pine, maple. H. 40 W. 48 D. 21½

Typical of seventeenth century design are the compart-mentalization of the two large drawers (giving the appearance of four small ones) and the applied ebonized ornament. How-ever, the panels of this chest are distinctively carved with large, stylized, so-called sunflowers and tulips.[34] Thirty-nine exam-ples of sunflower furniture — cupboards, drawerless chests and one- and two-drawer chests — survive. There is strong evi-dence that these pieces were made by Peter Blin.[35]

34. The sunflower is perhaps a Tudor rose adapted from English sources (Kirk, *Connecticut Furniture*, p. xiii).
35. Kane, pp. 74–77; Randall, No. 9.

33   **High Chest**   B.69.43

Boston, 1695–1715
Burled walnut, pine. H. 68½ W. 40 D. 22¼

The high chest was a new form at the end of the seven-teenth century. This example has a balanced architectural com-position with bold cornice and molding above a pulvinated frieze — a treatment associated with the Ionic order. The sur-face is skillfully veneered with burled walnut on the facade, frieze and sides. Below, the cup-turned legs rebate sharply to delicate thin diameters.[36]

36. Related examples are at Yale University, the Garvan Collection (Kirk, *Early American Furniture*, p. 83); the Museum of Fine Arts, Boston (Randall, No. 51); Winterthur (Winchester, p. 15).

17

34 One-Drawer Chest   B.69.48

Massachusetts, probably Boston, 1690–1710
Oak, pine. H.31 W.47 D.21½

This example is related to a number of one-drawer chests with geometric panels. All are constructed with double-paneled ends and have cleat and peg hinges. Similar large spindles with long tops are used.[37] The panels on the earliest of these chests are decorated with small spindles while the later examples are painted contrasting colors.[38] None of them, however, has painted figured ornament as here. There has been obvious repainting in the nineteenth century when the ends and possibly the front central octagonal panel were grained. The highly stylized Tudor roses also appear to be a later embellishment. The drawer of this chest has been made with well-articulated dovetails, a practice limited to Boston at this early date.[39]

37. Randall, No. 12; Nutting, No. 45; Forman, Fig. 6; Winchester, p. 289.
38. Randall, p. 14.
39. Forman, pp. 12–16.

35 Desk   B.69.42

Boston area, 1700–1725
Burled walnut, pine. H.41¼ W.35 D.19½ (closed)
33½ (open)

The fully developed slant-top desk, an outgrowth of the desk-box-on-frame, first appeared during the William and Mary period. The example here is veneered with burled walnut. Walnut herringbone banding is applied around the drawer edges and vertically across the center of the drawers, visually compartmentalizing them into smaller units. Similar treatment appears on the slant lid. The interior is fitted with a well, and the writing surface shows signs of having been covered originally with leather or baize.[40]

40. The lid of a similar desk is recessed for a baize inset (Randall, No. 55). Like that desk, the ball feet of the Bayou Bend example are restorations.

The Queen Anne Period 1725-1760

The Queen Anne period represents the second phase of the English baroque. Throughout the late 1680's and 1690's, following the 1685 revocation of the Edict of Nantes, many French Protestant artisans emigrated to both Holland and England. Repeating a phenomenon of the 1660's Restoration, when the presence of foreign craftsmen had altered English taste, these immigrants also introduced strong continental influences. One of the most important figures in this transfer of primarily French fashion was Daniel Marot (ca. 1662–1752), a Huguenot who studied under Pierre Lepautre and worked at the court of Louis XIV. Upon leaving France he entered the service of Prince William of Orange, becoming Minister of Works. Although his later work shows a blending of Dutch and French taste, his magnificent designs for furniture and the decoration of royal chambers were for the most part conceived in the baroque style of Louis XIV. These designs were published in 1702 and again, in an enlarged edition, in 1712.[1]

Marot's work incorporated broad unified compositions, with bold surface planes and classical ornament. He introduced the s-shaped cabriole leg, derived from French and ultimately Italian prototypes, and made extensive use of curved lines, scrolls and shells. His concepts were particularly noticeable in chair design, where the tall back of curved outline, enclosing a vase-shape splat, was introduced.[2] Throughout the reigns of Queen Anne (1702–1714) and George I (1714–1727) this Franco-Dutch style was the fashion. Even later, the continued importance of the curved line is reflected by William Hogarth's extensive consideration of the cyma recta, or "line of beauty," in his satirical 1742 essay, *The Analysis of Beauty*.

During the 1720's a circle of cognoscenti, led by the third Earl of Burlington (1694–1753), began to disseminate the classical architectural style of Andrea Palladio (1518–1580). These neo-Palladians subscribed to strict classical architectural principles. Their rules of taste were applied equally to furniture. A leader of this movement, William Kent (1685–1748), designed furniture which he deemed appropriate for his classical buildings. His case pieces incorporated architectural detail: pilasters, broken-scrolled pediments and urn finials. During the reign of George II (1727-1760), baroque and neo-Palladian designs were made concurrently.

This second phase of the English baroque began to appear in the colonies during the 1720's, as the elaborately carved and small-patterned surfaces of William and Mary were replaced by plainer, broadly grained ones. The curved lines of Daniel Marot were adopted, particularly in chair design. Turned legs were succeeded by s-shape cabrioles, which terminated in three major types of foot — pad, slipper and trifid (Nos. 36, 60, 45). In addition, the Portuguese or paintbrush foot was occasionally retained (No. 63), and other minor variations were also used; about 1750, the ball and claw foot began to appear (No. 47). Shells and scrolls became important decorative details (Nos. 48, 68). Two new furniture forms, the tea table and card table, were introduced (Nos. 59, 57), and at the end of the period a small number of upholstered sofas began to appear.

Regional differences in the interpretation of the style were marked, especially in chair design. The New England expression was considerably more vertical and rectangular, while New York and Philadelphia design conformed more closely to Marot prototypes (No. 46). Inlaid ornament found special favor in New England (No. 63). Case pieces, high chests and desk and bookcases, reflecting neo-Palladian influence, were made with architectural scrolled pediments, finials and occasionally pilasters (No. 68). During the 1750's, elements of rococo design began to be overlaid on existing forms (No. 49), anticipating the advent of the Chippendale style in the following decade.

1. *Oeuvres Du Sr. D. Marot . . . Contenant plussiers penssez utiles aux architects, peintres, sculpteurs, orfeures & jardiniers & autres; les toutes en faveure de ceux qui s'appliquerent aux beaux arts,* A. la Haye, 1702, Chez Pierre Husson. This was republished in a second enlarged edition in 1712.

2. Ralph Fastnedge, *English Furniture Styles from 1500 to 1830,* Harmondsworth, Middlesex, Penguin Books, Ltd., 1955, Pl. 19.

THE QUEEN ANNE SITTING ROOM.   This room incorporates Salem, Massachusetts, woodwork from the third quarter of the eighteenth century. Stylistically, the mantel and over-mantel frame were new features introduced about 1760. The soft blue-green has been matched to the original paint color. Dutch aubergine delft tiles with biblical scenes are set around the fireplace opening. Eighteenth century delft ware, part of a large collection of both Dutch and English origin, appears on the mantel shelf and in the cupboard at the right. Also at the right is a portrait of *John Gerry* by Joseph Badger. A pastel of *Sarah Henshaw* by John Singleton Copley hangs over the mantel. The furniture is from Philadelphia and New England. On the floor is a Kuba carpet.

THE QUEEN ANNE BEDROOM.   The paneling here, with its original light blue paint, was first installed in an Ipswich, Massachusetts, house built circa 1740. In this room are New England Queen Anne examples of furniture. English crewel, worked in polychrome colors, covers the bed. The portrait of *William Holmes* was painted in Charleston by John Wollaston. The rose color of his waistcoat is the predominant hue of the large Kuba carpet.

36 Side Chair (one of a pair)   B.69.247
    Boston, 1740–1760
    Walnut, maple. H. 39¾ W. 20½ D. 20½

These chairs were once plain walnut examples of the
most typical Massachusetts type.[3] The yoke crest, straight stiles,
vase splat, rectangular seat and block and spindle stretchers are
all characteristic. Sometime later — perhaps as early as 1790,
but more likely about 1820 — these chairs were painted with
black and gold "eastern" ornament. The leaves on the skirt
relate closely to painted decoration of Empire furniture,
strengthening a circa 1820 date. Although family tradition
states that the chairs were sent to the Orient, the painting is
obviously western and was probably executed in Boston. The
arms are those of Samuel P. Gardner, in the family of whose
niece, Eliza Blanchard Winthrop, the chairs descended.[4]

   3. A second pair is at Historic Deerfield (*Antiques*, September 1956,
p. 234); the third in the collection of Mrs. Charles L. Bybee, Houston
(*Antiques*, January 1968, p. 76).
   4. Fales, *Painted Furniture*, p. 67.

37 Side Chair   B.57.75
    Newport, Rhode Island, 1730–1750
    Walnut, maple. H. 44 W. 19 D. 21

This example retains the vertical proportions of the
earlier William and Mary style. Typical of New England is the
continued use of strengthening stretchers. Turned back legs,
bold c-scrolls on the front upper leg and extremely thin pad
feet are features that appear on an early Newport chair.[5] Another Newport chair in a private collection is virtually identical
to this example but has rounded rather than flat stiles.[6]

   5. *Rhode Island Furniture*, No. 2.
   6. Kirk, *American Chairs*, No. 161, also No. 160; an identical pair is
privately owned (Weston, Massachusetts).

38 Side Chair (one of a pair)   B.60.31
    Newport, Rhode Island, 1730–1750
    Walnut, maple. H. 42 W. 19½ D. 21¾

Although flat stretchers are seen in English chairs, in
America they seem to be peculiar to Newport and, occasionally,
Philadelphia. Molded scrolling of the upper leg and lambre-
quins at the knees are also features seen in Newport examples.[7]

   7. Downs, No. 110; Randall, No. 133.

39 Side Chair   B.60.51
Newport, Rhode Island, 1730–1750
Walnut, maple. H.40 W.22 D.21

Although similar to the preceding two examples, this chair with its broader, less vertical proportions and horseshoe-shaped seat is later in concept. The round shoulder or semicircular loop at the top of the stiles is not common. Derived from Chinese prototypes, this treatment was popular in England at the turn of the eighteenth century; in America it was restricted to Newport furniture. A chair matching this example is at Colonial Williamsburg, and a third is in a private collection.[8]

8. *Rhode Island Furniture*, No. 4.

40 Side Chair (one of a pair)   B.58.141
Newport, Rhode Island, 1750–1780
Walnut, maple. H.38⅜ W.21 D.16½

Bold baroque shells with scrolled edges, strategically placed as accents on the crest and knees, relate this chair to the shell-ornamented case pieces made by the Townsend-Goddard school. Curved stiles, the vigorous outline of the splat and small heavily webbed claw feet are features of late Newport examples. Blocks at the ends of the ringed spindle stretchers are not common but are known on several other chairs with Newport provenance.[9]

9. Carpenter, No. 5; Downs, No. 103, is a related example; also the Metropolitan Museum, New York, Acc. No. 10.125.696.

41 Side Chair   B.69.218
Connecticut, Norwich area, 1730–1760
Cherry, maple. H.40¾ W.22 D.20

The stiff vertical lines of the back are relieved by the curved profile of the eared splat, a feature more commonly seen in Philadelphia examples. Also unusual is the omission of a medial stretcher. A matching side chair is at Winterthur and an armchair with the same details is in a private collection.[10]

10. Kirk, *American Chairs*, Nos. 187–188; for a more detailed discussion of the armchair, see Kirk, *Connecticut Furniture*, No. 232.

42 Side Chair   B.69.33

New York, 1740–1770
Mahogany, ash, pine, maple. H.41¾ W.22½ D.22

Generous proportions, a heavy seat rail and shaped terminals of the rear legs are commonly found in Queen Anne
chairs of New York. Unique to this set is the cypher *RML*
carved into the splat.[11] The chairs descended in the Livingston
family and were traditionally owned by Robert and Margaret
Beekman Livingston, who were married in 1742. However,
their son Robert married Mary Stevens in 1770, and possibly
the initials refer to the younger couple. If made for the parents,
the chairs represent an early use of both mahogany and ball
and claw feet. Techniques of construction and ornament suggest that the chairs are the product of a country craftsman.[12]
They, therefore, would have been made somewhat later than
their style suggests.

11. This chair is marked *III* on the back seat rail. Four chairs from the
same set are in museum collections: Yale University, the Garvan Col-
lection (Kirk, *American Chairs*, No. 127); Museum of the City of New
York; Winterthur (*Antiques*, December 1970, pp. 904, 906); the Art
Institute of Chicago (*Calendar of the Art Institute of Chicago*, Vol. 66,
No. 2, March 1972, p. 11). Three others are in private collections.

12. *Antiques*, December 1970, p. 906. For an extensive discussion of
these chairs, see Kirk, *American Chairs*, p. 43.

43 Side Chair   B.69.69

Philadelphia, 1740–1760
Walnut, pine. H.40 W.19¾ D.20¼

A simple yoke-shape cresting outlined with beaded
molding places this chair earlier in terms of design than the
following example. Lambrequins ornament the knees.[13] The
sharp inward curve and squared foot of the rear legs is an unusual feature that is seen on a pair of armchairs at Winterthur.[14]

13. This sort of ornament appears on a side chair labeled by William
Savery (Comstock, No. 176); also on a dressing table which descended
in the Savery family (*Pennsylvania Museum Bulletin*, January 1925, p. 62).
Chairs of this sort have been widely ascribed to Savery.

14. Downs, Nos. 28, 111.

44 Side Chair (one of a pair)   B.69.407

Philadelphia, 1740–1760
Walnut, pine. H.42¾ W.20 D.19¾

The crest rail has been extended vertically and ornamented with a carved shell, a motif repeated at the knees. Occasionally, stretchers, either turned or flat and shaped as here,
were used in the Philadelphia Queen Anne, but they are considerably thinner than Newport examples (No. 38). Each of
these chairs is branded *G E* on the back seat rail, possibly for
George Emlen (1695–1754).

45 Side Chair   B.69.246

Philadelphia, 1740–1760
Walnut, pine. H.42½ W.21 D.19¾

Extra ornament not only increased the visual delight of
a Queen Anne style chair but also added to the cost. This
Philadelphia example has been embellished with volutes and
a shell at the crest, and shells with husks at the knees. The winged
splat has a particularly vigorous outline. Well-defined trifid
feet are a type which, although used occasionally elsewhere,
was favored in the Philadelphia area.

46 Side Chair   B.69.65

Philadelphia, 1740–1760
Walnut, pine. H.42 W.20 D.20½

With its fluid, harmonious composition this chair is one
of the finest expressions of the Philadelphia Queen Anne style.
The scrolled ruffle on the knee brackets is rare.[15] The stiles are
round in section, a refined detail. Richly figured walnut has
been veneered on the spooned splat.

15. Similarly carved knee brackets appear on a chair at Winterthur
(Downs, No. 122); as well as on another (Hornor, Pl. 68).

47 Side Chair (one of a pair)   B.69.76

Philadelphia, 1750–1770
Mahogany, pine. H.42¾ W.22 D.20½

The pierced interlaced splat is a pre-*Director* type popular both in Philadelphia and elsewhere (No. 81). The carved
shell, with asymmetrical leafage, is no longer contained within
the crest but breaks out above.[16] This pair is part of a larger set
at Winterthur.[17]

16. The same ornament appears on a fully Chippendale example at
Yale University, the Garvan Collection (Kirk, *American Chairs*, No. 68).
17. Downs, No. 117; Hornor, Pl. 81.

48 Armchair
B.69.249

Philadelphia, 1740–1760
Walnut, pine. H. 43½ W. 33 D. 21

The controlled dynamic composition of the best Philadelphia Queen Anne armchairs places them in a class by themselves, as this example illustrates. The pierced motifs of the winged splat and the incised sections of the trifid feet are rare.[18]

18. A side chair, identical save for the knee brackets, is in the Brush-Everhard House at Colonial Williamsburg (Winchester, p. 74). The same foot treatment appears on a side chair at Winterthur (*Antiques*, December 1970, p. 906).

49 Armchair
B.69.2

Philadelphia, 1755–1770
Mahogany, pine. H. 42¾ W. 31 D. 22½

This chair represents the ultimate enrichment of the Queen Anne form. Acanthus carving on the splat and legs anticipates Chippendale designs. Crowning the back is a large shell-shaped palmette pierced to reveal a diapered background. Another chair of this design is at the Metropolitan Museum, New York, and despite minor variations in dimensions and carving of the paw feet and arm terminals, that example must be from the same shop.[19]

19. Downs, *Picture Book*, No. 11.

50 Corner Chair
B.69.250

Philadelphia, ca. 1750
Walnut, maple. H. 31 W. 32½ D. 30½

The corner or roundabout chair was introduced to America about 1720. This example has curved arm supports in the Philadelphia style, which echo the cabriole of the legs below. The unusually narrow vase splats are in proportion to their height. Beading along the upper edges of the legs forms an angular lambrequin below the knees. Although the feet have a unique pointed profile, there is evidence that, originally, thin toes formed a trifid foot and have since been broken or removed.[20] Original brown cowhide covers the seat.

20. A similar example is in the Metropolitan Museum, New York (R. T. H. Halsey and C. O. Cornelius, *A Handbook of the American Wing Opening Exhibition*, New York, The Metropolitan Museum of Art, 1924, p. 111).

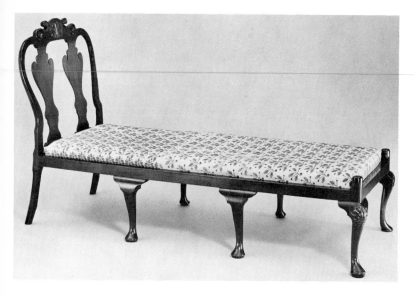

51 Couch   B.59.81

Philadelphia, 1740–1760
Mahogany. H.41 W.27¾ L.67½

The couch, or daybed, continued to be made during the Queen Anne period, although survivals today are not common. In design, this example is related to the most fully developed Philadelphia chairs.[21] Pad feet with rings are typical of that city.

21. Illustrated, Hornor, Pl. 60.

52 Easy Chair   B.59.95

Massachusetts, 1740–1760
Walnut, maple. H.48 W.34½ D.27½

In New England, the arms of Queen Anne easy chairs ceased to have horizontal scrolls and were made with vertical cone-shaped rolls. The use of stretchers followed practices observed in side chairs.

53 Easy Chair   B.69.252

Possibly Newport, Rhode Island, 1730–1750
Maple. H.48 W.33¾ D.29

C-scroll arms and a ball and ring stretcher, both earlier features, have been retained here. The design of the front feet and rear leg is like that of a Rhode Island side chair (No. 37). Similar ornament appears on the front legs of both examples, suggesting that this easy chair may be an early Newport example.[22]

22. *Rhode Island Furniture*, Nos. 2, 3, 6.

54 Easy Chair

B.66.1

Newport, Rhode Island, 1740–1760
Maple. H.38½ W.27 D.26

Although following the form favored throughout New England, the large flattened pad feet with cushion underneath are not unlike those seen in Rhode Island examples (No. 38), and the shell at the knee is of the type favored in Newport (No. 40).[23]

23. A closely related Newport example is at Winterthur (Downs, No. 80).

55 Easy Chair

B.69.251

Philadelphia, 1740–1760
Walnut, maple, cherry. H.48⅜ W.34 D.28½

Although cabriole rear legs are usually associated with furniture of English origin, a small number of American examples exist. Some of those are from Philadelphia.[24] The pad foot with a ring is a typical Philadelphia type, as is the semicircular seat frame front. The beaded molding and c-scroll on the front legs appear on several other examples with Philadelphia provenance.[25] Only the vertically rolled arms are inexplicable in terms of known Philadelphia examples.

24. Downs, Nos. 77–78; for a Massachusetts Chippendale example, see *Antiques*, January 1968, p. 78.

25. Hornor, Pl. 311; Comstock, No. 206; Downs, No. 269.

56 Drop-Leaf Table

B.69.220

Boston, 1730–1760
Walnut, pine, maple. H.25 W.30 D.28½

The drop-leaf table was made in varying sizes from small multipurpose versions to larger dining tables. This example, with a scalloped skirt, has the thin, conservative cabriole legs and delicate ankles favored in New England.[26] Unusual is the hock at the back of each foot called, in the eighteenth century, a horsebone foot. The table has a history of ownership by Isaac Smith (1719–1787) of Boston and was probably made there.

26. A related example is at Winterthur (Downs, No. 304).

57 Card Table *(opposite)*   B.69.406

Boston, 1730–1750
Mahogany, pine.
H. 26¾ W. 36¾ D. 16¼ (closed) 32 (open)

Introduction of the card table about 1725 reflected the widespread enthusiasm for gambling and card games. The form has a folding top, often dished for candlesticks and fitted with wells for counters. Usually, the open flap is supported by a rear leg which swings out like a gate. Here, however, following a sophisticated English practice which provided support in a more sightly manner, the back legs are hinged to a folding framework which, when open, forms an extension of the skirt. This treatment, called accordian or concertina action, is rare on American tables, but another closely related Boston example is similarly constructed.[27] The top is fitted with original crewel embroidery. Checker inlay, as on the top and skirt, was popular in Massachusetts Queen Anne furniture (No. 67). The turreted ends and slender legs are also typical of Massachusetts. The table belonged to Peter Faneuil (1700–1742) and relates stylistically to two other Boston examples with similar needlework.[28]

27. Randall, No. 79.
28. Museum of Fine Arts, Boston (Randall, No. 80); Pilgrim Hall, Plymouth (Rose Griggs, *A Catalogue of the Collection of the Pilgrim Society*, No. 245). The latter example, made for Mercy Otis Warren (1728–1815) of Plymouth, not only has a needlework top but relates stylistically to the Faneuil table, although it lacks a concertina action.

58 Card Table   B.69.132

Boston, 1750–1770
Mahogany, pine.
H. 26½ W. 36½ D. 18½ (closed) 35¼ (open)

The large turreted corners, flanked by vertical scrolls and almost straight thin cabriole legs, relate this table to the preceding example as well as to the turret-top tea table (No. 61). Although the c-scrolls at the knees are typical of Newport furniture, they occur in Massachusetts as well.[29] This treatment compares with two other Boston examples.[30]

29. Downs, No. 347.
30. Randall, No. 57; Hipkiss, No. 50.

59 Tea Table   B.69.349

Connecticut, probably Hartford, 1740–1770
Cherry, pine. H. 26 W. 20½ D. 29½

After 1725, as the consumption of tea became more common, a new form of table was introduced. It was characteristically rectangular with a molded top. Here the top of the leg projects very little at the knee, a feature often seen in Connecticut examples. Also typical of Connecticut is the boldly scalloped skirt. This table, which was traditionally owned by Dr. Ezekiel Porter (1707–1775) of Wethersfield, is nearly identical to one owned by the Talcott family of Hartford and must be from the same shop.[31]

31. Kirk, *Connecticut Furniture*, No. 158.

60 Tea Table

Newport, Rhode Island, 1740–1760
Mahogany. H.25½ W.20⅝ D.31¼

Delicate cabriole legs suggest a New England provenance while sharp-edged knees and long pointed slipper feet, also seen in Newport high chests, further pinpoint the origin of this tea table. It is one of at least five known examples.[32] The severe straight skirt with convex molding is similar to a later table, also in the Bayou Bend Collection (No. 105).

32. Carpenter, No. 74; *Antiques*, August 1961, p. 88; Schwartz, p. 50; *The Lansdell K. Christie Collection*, New York, Sotheby Parke Bernet, October 21, 1972, No. 72; a fifth table, although published as a Philadelphia example, is so similar as to be obviously also of Newport origin (Hornor, Pl. 47); another example, possibly one of the above, is in a private Delaware collection (*Special Loan Exhibits*, p. 49).

61 Tea Table

Boston, 1750–1770
Mahogany, maple. H.27 W.32 D.23½

Five tea tables with turreted frame are known today.[33] All vary slightly in details. The design, unique to these tables, is related stylistically to turreted card tables of the Boston area. While the origin of the shaped molded top is not clear, similarity to English tripod supper tables with round tops, ringed for dishes, suggests a possible inspiration.

33. At the Museum of Fine Arts, Boston (Randall, No. 31; Hipkiss, No. 60); Winterthur (Downs, No. 370); Historic Deerfield. All have 14 turrets except the Winterthur table, which has 12.

62 Tea Table

Philadelphia, 1750–1770
Mahogany. H.28 DIAM.30

About the middle of the eighteenth century the round, tripod pedestal tea table was introduced as an alternative to the rectangular type. This early example is in the late Queen Anne style. The shells at the knees and pendant husks, often seen on Queen Anne chairs, also ornament a rectangular tea table made for the Norris family. That example has the same flattened ball feet with heavily webbed claws.[34] The inverted baluster shaft is unusual but is known on two similar examples. A slightly later small stand at the Metropolitan Museum, New York, has a related pedestal.[35]

34. Hornor, Pl. 74.
35. Downs, *Picture Book*, No. 27.

63   Dressing Table   B.69.134

       Massachusetts, 1730–1760
       Walnut, pine. H. 29¾ W. 33¼ D. 20½

    The skirt with drops, the delicate legs and the concave drawer of this dressing table are all typical of New England. Patterned stringing and inlays relate closely to a group of distinguished Massachusetts examples.[36] The paintbrush feet, a *retardetaire* feature most commonly seen in Queen Anne examples from the Philadelphia area, are not unlike those of a Boston japanned high chest.[37]

    36. Hipkiss, No. 18; Randall, No. 53; Downs, No. 190; Nutting, No. 400; Winchester, p. 243.
    37. Downs, No. 188.

64   Dressing Table   B.65.4

       New Hampshire, 1725–1760
       Maple, walnut, pine. H. 31 W. 38½ D. 19½

    The unusual skirt of this dressing table follows William and Mary design. Similar wide proportions appear on another dressing table, and a "tuckaway" tea table has very similar legs.[38] Both these other pieces are believed to have been made in New Hampshire.

    38. Randall, *New Hampshire*, No. 21; Randall, No. 83.

65   Dressing Table   B.59.70

       Connecticut, 1740–1760
       Cherry, pine. H. 33½ W. 36 D. 19¾

    Although acquired thirty-one years after No. 69, this dressing table is identical except for the hardware and was obviously made in the same shop.

66   Dressing Table   B.69.238

Pennsylvania or New Jersey, 1740–1770
Maple, poplar, pine. H. 29 W. 31¾ D. 20¼

The arched skirt and drawer arrangement of this example appear on a group of Portuguese-footed dressing tables made in southern New Jersey and rural Pennsylvania.[39]

39. Downs, No. 322; Comstock, No. 222; Schiffer, Fig. 114.

67   High Chest   B.69.221

Massachusetts, 1735–1745
Maple, walnut, pine. H. 66¾ W. 36¼ D. 20

Highly figured walnut veneering creates a flame-like pattern across the facade of this high chest.[40] Each drawer is inlaid with a checker pattern similar to that of the card table made for Peter Faneuil (No. 57) and a Boston desk and bookcase.[41] The inlaid concave niche relates to the treatment of No. 63.

40. A later but related example is at the Museum of Fine Arts, Boston (Randall, No. 54). Vertical inlay on the center of the drawers visually compartmentalizes that piece, but the treatment of figured walnut is similar.

41. Hipkiss, No. 18.

68   High Chest (*opposite*)   B.69.348

Boston, 1740–1750
Maple, pine, paint, gesso. H. 92½ W. 41 D. 23¾

Painting in imitation of Oriental lacquer, called japanning, was very popular in Boston prior to 1750. It is represented here in its final, most sophisticated stage, consisting of gilt figures and gesso applied against a tortoise-shell-like background. Two similar japanned high chests are known, one at Winterthur and one in the Metropolitan Museum, New York.[42] In both design and carved detail, this piece is closely related to the Metropolitan example.[43] However, the large scale of japanned ornament is more nearly like that of the Winterthur piece. A double-beaded molding around the drawer openings is not seen on either of the other two high chests. These similarities and differences indicate that the Bayou Bend chest complies with the patterns of Boston taste but cannot be assigned to a specific cabinetmaker or japanner.

42. The Winterthur example was made by John Pimm (Downs, No. 188); the Metropolitan piece is illustrated (Comstock, No. 184); a third related example with only traces of japanned ornament remaining is in the New Haven Colony Historical Society. Japanning is extremely fragile. The Bayou Bend chest has some restoration and regilding, but the designs are original.

43. They have the same pediments and gilded shells as several walnut-veneered high chests of Boston provenance (Randall, No. 54; Biddle, No. 55).

High Chest   B.28.1

Connecticut, 1740–1760
Cherry, pine. H. 82¾ W. 37¾ D. 19¾

This high chest has a history of ownership by Dr. Ezekiel Porter (1707–1775) of Wethersfield, Connecticut.[44] Stylistically, it is related to the most successful Connecticut high chests, and several of its details occur on other examples. The fans have arc terminals on each ray and curve inward at the bases. The distinctive triangular cuts at the base of the drops and tall, capped urn finials appear together on another cherry, bonnet-top high chest.[45]

44. This piece was in the Porter-Bidwell House in Wethersfield until circa 1913; then it was on loan at the Wadsworth Atheneum, Hartford, Connecticut, for about ten years. Later it was exhibited at Webb House, Wethersfield. It is illustrated (Lockwood, Fig. 92). Another high chest and dressing table with a similar history, but unrelated stylistically, are in the Brooklyn Museum (Kirk, *Connecticut Furniture*, Nos. 81, 129; Schwartz, Figs. 36, 37). Two chambers from the Porter-Bidwell House are also installed at the Brooklyn Museum as period rooms (Schwartz, p. 49).

45. Kirk, *Connecticut Furniture*, No. 84; also *George Dudley Seymour's Furniture Collection*, Hartford, Connecticut Historical Society, 1959, p. 55.

70   Desk-on-Frame   B.71.10

New England, 1740–1770
Cherry, pine. H. 40¾ W. 35½ D. 20½

The desk-on-frame, a survival of the earlier writing box-on-frame, was made concurrently with the conventional slant-top desk but is a far less common form. Delicate legs, sharp knees and flattened arches on the skirt indicate a New England origin for this example. The interior is extremely plain, with drawers having small finger holes rather than pulls.

71   Desk-on-Frame   B.61.82

Philadelphia, 1730–1760
Walnut, poplar, pine. H.42½ W.38½ D.21

Philadelphia desks-on-frame, related in design to dressing tables, usually have vigorously scalloped skirts. While the
line of the skirt and chamfered corners are the only ornament
of the otherwise severe exterior, the interior is elaborate, with
two tiers of serpentine drawers flanking a central paneled
door.[46]

46. A related example is in the Lammot du Pont Copeland collection
(Biddle, No. 61); a second, with bookcase, is illustrated (Hornor, Pl. 35);
a third slightly later example is at Winterthur (Downs, No. 220).

72   Spice or Valuable Box   B.65.8

Pennsylvania, 1740–1770
Walnut, poplar, pine. H.25⅝ W.16⅛ D.10¼

Small cabinets with nests of drawers behind locking
doors were made in quantity in the rural area surrounding
Philadelphia. Although today they are usually called "spice"
chests, it is likely that various other sorts of valuables also were
stored in the multiple small drawers. The doors of conventional
flat-topped examples were occasionally embellished with applied panels like those used on clock case bases.[47] The similarity
here to the hood of a clock, perhaps a parallel relationship
although rare, is found in several other later examples.[48]

47. *Special Loan Exhibits*, pp. 89–90.
48. *Special Loan Exhibits*, p. 99; also *Antiques*, October 1939, p. 175.

THE DRAWING ROOM. The neo-Palladian style of the late Georgian era is reflected in the architecture of the drawing room. The projecting chimney breast with mantel and crossetted frame above is similar to those of the great Philadelphia country houses such as Mount Pleasant or Cliveden, while the scrolled pediments of the doorways are based on those at Shirley Plantation on the James River, Virginia. The room is filled with furniture made in the cities of the Atlantic seaboard. Above the mantel is a Vaughan-type portrait of *George Washington* painted by Gilbert Stuart for the Patterson family of Baltimore. An English Worcester porcelain service of the Dr. Wall Period is on the tea table. Also of English origin are the chandeliers. A Kirman garden-type rug covers the floor.

The Chippendale Period 1760-1790

Throughout the first two centuries of its development, America depended heavily on printed sources for knowledge of new fashion and design. The rococo style was introduced by several design books, the best known of which was *The Gentleman and Cabinet-Maker's Director* (1754) by Thomas Chippendale (1718–1779). Today the American rococo period bears his name.

The rococo style originated in France during the 1720's. The French expression of the new taste used naturalistic forms — rocks, shells, flowers and fruit — arranged with scrolls in asymmetrical fantasy. The term rococo is derived from *rocaille*, meaning rock or grotto work, which referred to fantastic garden structures where the style originated. Elements of the French or Modern style (as Chippendale called it) began to appear in England in the 1730's, and by 1740 Matthias Locke published rococo designs in his *New Drawing Book of Ornaments, Shields, Compartments, Masks, etc.* His *Six Sconces* of 1744 and *Six Tables* of 1746 were further adaptations of French taste to English furniture design. During the 1750's a restrained version of the rococo became the accepted London mode.

In 1754, Thomas Chippendale, a London cabinetmaker, published his famous *Director*. This volume, consisting of 160 plates and descriptive notes, was basically a trade catalogue and advertisement depicting furniture in the prevailing London style. As the first complete and comprehensive pattern book for furniture, however, it is tremendously important. Primarily, it illustrated examples of the French or Modern taste (the rococo) but also included designs of the Gothic and Chinese styles reflecting earlier trends in English garden architecture. The book met with great success and was reprinted in 1755. Seven years later a third, revised edition was issued.

The *Director* appeared in America at a relatively early date. A copy was owned by Thomas Affleck, a Scottish-born cabinetmaker who emigrated to Pennsylvania with Governor John Penn in 1763 (No. 89). Although the book served as an important catalogue of the new taste and was used throughout the colonies, American cabinetmakers rarely copied any one design in its entirety. Rather, they adapted the vocabulary of ornament to the prevailing regional style.

Chippendale's, however, was not the only rococo design book to be used in America. *Household Furniture* (1760), published by the Society of Upholsterers and Cabinet-Makers, and *Universal System of Household Furniture* (1759–1763), issued by William Ince and John Mayhew, were also widely circulated. Robert Manwaring's *The Cabinet and Chair Maker's Real Friend and Companion* (1765) was another important design source, especially in New England.

If the English expression of the rococo was considerably less exuberant than that of the French, the quality of restraint was even more evident in the American interpretation. With the exception of chairs, rococo detail was limited to an overlay of ornament on existing forms (No. 110). Usually designs were balanced and symmetrical, but occasionally pure rococo asymmetry appeared (Nos. 80, 125). C- and s-scrolls were often interlaced with shells or naturalistic leafage (Nos. 119, 131). In accordance with Chippendale's precepts, motifs of Chinese or Gothic inspiration also were utilized. The cabriole leg continued to be used extensively, usually terminating in a ball and claw foot. Furniture with Chinese or Gothic overtones, however, often featured straight legs, called "Marlborough" in Philadelphia (No. 111). In chairs, the controlled curves and smooth surfaces of the preceding Queen Anne style exploded into nervous outlines and highly ornamented surfaces.

The high chest of drawers, by then obsolete in England, continued to be made in America; it found particular favor in Philadelphia. There the purest rococo detail was used in ornamenting the pediments and bases of what became, accordingly, a uniquely American form. The block-front furniture of New England, however, was apart from the mainstream of rococo furniture (Nos. 123, 130). Although made throughout the Chippendale era, it continued the baroque traditions of the preceding Queen Anne period.

Seeds of the subsequent Federal style began to appear in the 1770's, and by the 1780's furniture became lighter in scale, often with tapering legs (No. 112). These developments foreshadowed the sharp break with the past when the new Adamesque style became accepted in the years following the American Revolution.

THE PHILADELPHIA HALL. Examples of furniture made in Philadelphia in the years spanning the American Revolution fill the central hall of the house. To the left of the garden door is a portrait of Texas Governor *James Stephen Hogg* (1852–1906), father of Bayou Bend's donor. The beige, blue and rose tones of the large Kirman carpet are repeated in the brocade on the chairs.

THE CHIPPENDALE BEDROOM.   The molded cornice, plaster walls and paneled dado
are typical of interiors during the second half of the eighteenth century. The putty color, called
"stone" by contemporaries, was popular in the Chippendale period. On the bed is an Indian
painted cotton chintz or palampore made about 1750. The bed hangings and matching curtains
are made of red wool moreen. Similar color has been used in the Ghiordes rug from Turkey.
The provenance of the furniture is New England and the Middle Atlantic Colonies.

THE NEWPORT ROOM. The northeast parlor of the Nichols-Wanton-Hunter House was reproduced in abbreviated form as a setting for Newport furniture. Bold paneling, painted pale green, echoes the baroque forms of Rhode Island block-front furniture. On the tea table are polychrome examples of saltglaze stoneware, part of an extensive collection. Seventeenth and eighteenth century silver appears in the cupboard. The portrait of *John Rindge* (1695–1740) has been attributed to Peter Pelham (1695–1751). Deep reds and blue predominate in the eighteenth century Isfahan carpet.

THE MASSACHUSETTS ROOM. Rich dark blue paneling forms the setting for Chippendale examples from Massachusetts. Similar vibrant color appears in the eighteenth century needlework embroidery of the easy chair on the left and the polychrome Liverpool delft tiles at the fireplace opening. A seventeenth century Caucasian dragon rug, the earliest in the Collection, covers the floor. Whieldon and agate wares made in Staffordshire, England, are set on the tea table in the foreground, and other examples are on the stands at the left and right.

73   Side Chair (one of a pair)   B.69.135
       Boston, ca. 1760–1765
       Mahogany, pine, ash.   H.36½   W.24   D.21½

      Blunt molded ears, the sharp profile at the knees and a retracted claw foot are all features which indicate a Massachusetts origin. The interlaced, scrolled splat is derived from designs of Robert Manwaring. Although used elsewhere, it found its widest acceptance in Massachusetts (Nos. 74 and 94).

      Block and spindle stretchers, a conservative feature retained from earlier styles, are typical of the New England Chippendale. These chairs, made in Boston, bear an inscription that they were owned by Massachusetts Lieutenant Governor Thomas Hutchinson. The inscription further relates that they were saved from his residence in Garden Court Street when, on August 6, 1765, during the Stamp Act riots, it was sacked by the Sons of Liberty.

74   Side Chair (one of eight)   B.69.361
       Boston or Salem, 1765–1775
       Mahogany, maple.   H.38   W.23½   D.21¾

      These chairs are *en suite* with a double chair-back settee (No. 94). They are virtually the same design as No. 73, varying only in such details as a slip seat, acanthus carving at the knees and the raked-back claws, a second type of Massachusetts foot.

75   Side Chair   B.57.71
       Newport, Rhode Island, 1760–1780
       Mahogany, maple.   H.38⅛   W.20   D.19½

      Cabled fluting on the legs relates to both a Newport easy chair (No. 92) and card table (No. 108). The complicated scrolled splat, with cross-hatching and punchwork, appears on a number of Rhode Island chairs.[1]

     1. Kirk, *American Chairs*, No. 182; *Rhode Island Furniture*, No. 12; Bishop, No. 202; Carpenter, No. 4; Hanks, No. 45.

76   Side Chair (one of a pair)   B.69.138
Norwich, Connecticut, 1760–1790
Cherry. H.37 W.20 D.19⅝

These chairs traditionally were owned by Christopher
Leffingwell (1734–1810) of Norwich, Connecticut.[2] The needlework seats are believed to have been worked by his wife,
Margaret, whose initials *MML* appear in ink on one of the seat
frames. Blunt ears and the thin splat design are Massachusetts
details.[3] However, the proportions and treatment of the straight
legs, with simplified Chinese-style brackets (one missing) and
molded stretchers, relate to a documented Norwich example.[4]
This fact, coupled with their history of local ownership, suggest
a Norwich provenance.

2. He inherited a large house in Norwich, which he remodeled in the
1760's (*Antiques*, June 1961, p. 567).
3. Kirk, *American Chairs*, Nos. 119–120.
4. Kirk, *Connecticut Furniture*, No. 246.

77   Side Chair   B.69.34
New York, 1760–1790
Mahogany, cherry, ash. H.39⅜ W.23½ D.22½

This chair is one of a famous set at one time thought to
have been made by Gilbert Ash for Sir William Johnson.[5]
Attribution to Ash, however, was based on an inscribed example at Winterthur, for which the inscription is no longer considered authentic. Moreover, the history of ownership by Sir
William Johnson stemmed solely from a 1929 notarized statement by the then owner. An equally possible candidate for
ownership is Samuel Johnson, President of King's College
(1754–1763), father of William Samuel Johnson, Senator from
Connecticut and President of Columbia College (1787–1800).

Although it has a rounded seat, other features are in the
New York Chippendale style: squared rear feet, cross-hatching
at the knees, downturned scrolls at the knee blocks and a
lozenge within an interlaced splat. The finely carved shells on
the ears appear also on No. 79.

5. Other examples are at Winterthur (Downs, No. 149); Yale University, the Garvan Collection (Kirk, *American Chairs*, No. 143); the
collection of Stanley Stone, Milwaukee (Hanks, No. 29).

78   Side Chair   B.69.21
New York, ca. 1760–1780
Mahogany, pine, ash. H.38½ W.23⅞ D.22⅝

While lighter and slightly smaller than the norm, the
tassel and ruffle ornament of the splat relate this chair to other
New York examples.[6] The shaped rear legs and squared leaf
carving on the ears are features often found in chairs of New
York provenance. This example has unusually crisp, naturalistic
carving on the crest and distinctive spiral gadroon and leaf carving on the seat rail. The feet are small and relate to No. 77.

6. A large set was made for the van Rensselaer family (Downs, No. 52);
Kirk, *American Chairs*, Nos. 136–138.

79 Side Chair (one of a pair)   B.69.23
New York, 1760–1785
Mahogany, pine, cherry. H. 39¼ W. 23 D. 22

Perhaps the most distinctive feature of these chairs is the richly carved leafage which laps over the seat rail. Properly called a hipped leg, this rare detail occurs on several other New York examples and occasionally in Philadelphia.[7] Large, square ball and claw feet are typically New York. In an interesting departure from standard construction, the seat rails are mortised through the stiles.

7. One New York armchair is at Colonial Williamsburg (Kirk, *American Chairs,* No. 144); a related side chair is in the Henry Ford Museum, Dearborn (Bishop, No. 170); a Philadelphia example was made for the Maris-Gregg family (Hornor, Pl. 330).

80 Side Chair (one of a pair)   B.58.146
Philadelphia, ca. 1755–1770
Mahogany, pine. H. 40½ W. 23⅝ D. 22¼

The crests of these chairs are carved with asymmetrical rococo cartouche and naturalistic flowering branches. This detail is not unlike the more elaborate treatment of fully developed Chippendale examples.[8] Yet, the rococo ornament is controlled and contained within the crest in a manner similar to the treatment of the Philadelphia Queen Anne. The mate to this chair has mirror asymmetry; apparently they were originally part of a large set with alternating asymmetrical ornament.[9]

8. Hornor, Pls., 118–119; Downs, No. 137.
9. A third example is in a private Providence, Rhode Island, collection.

81 Side Chair (one of a pair)   B.69.77
Philadelphia, 1760–1790
Mahogany, pine. H. 39¾ W. 23½ D. 20¾

Repetition of the shell and volutes on the splat serves to unify the various parts of the composition, creating a very successful form. A matching chair is in the Garvan Collection at Yale University.[10]

10. Kirk, *American Chairs,* No. 69.

82   Side Chair   B.69.80

Philadelphia, 1765–1780
Mahogany, pine. H. 38½ W. 23½ D. 20¾

This example is more fully rococo than the preceding
Philadelphia chairs. The proportions are wider and lower, the
carved ears less pronounced. A considerably lighter and more
three-dimensional splat may have been derived in part from
Plate XI of the third edition of Chippendale's *Director*. Asymmetrical ornament and scrolls on the skirt relate to the treatment
on examples by Thomas Tufft and others associated with James
Gillingham.[11]

11. Downs, No. 134; Kirk, *American Chairs*, No. 85; Hipkiss, No. 88.

83   Armchair   B.57.95

Boston or Salem, 1765–1785
Mahogany, maple. H. 35 W. 29¾ D. 23

Although Chippendale armchairs of Massachusetts provenance are uncommon, this chair is related to several sophisticated Boston or Salem pieces, particularly an armchair owned
by Elias Hasket Derby.[12] Typical of Massachusetts are the
molding, which extends the crest rail over the stiles to the blunt
ears, the pointed knee of the cabriole leg and the retracted side
claw on the ball feet. Flat, double-kinked arms also appear on
other Massachusetts examples (No. 88). However, the absence
of stretchers and the wide low profile are unusual features. In
contrast to the otherwise severe design the crest is carved with
discreet rococo leafage.

12. Sack, *Opportunities*, January 1970, No. 1398; Kirk, *American Chairs*,
No. 123; Comstock, No. 246.

84   Armchair   B.69.30

New York, 1765–1785
Mahogany, ash, maple. H. 38½ W. 27⅝ D. 23¾

The exotic tastes of the Gothic and Chinese styles are
successfully blended in the back of this New York armchair.[13]
Straight legs with block feet further the Chinese appearance,
while leafage on the ears and at the ends of the arms adds a
rococo touch. Although the broad proportions and rounded
arm ends, which flow directly into the arm support, give this
chair an English appearance, the presence of ash and maple as
secondary woods confirms its American origin.

13. A pair of side chairs with similar splat and back is at Winterthur
(Downs, No. 143).

85 Armchair

B.69.18

Philadelphia, 1760–1785
Mahogany, pine. H.42¼ W.31¼ D.24½

Particularly notable are the well-conceived arms with bold scrolled ends and typical Philadelphia curved supports. A large enclosed shell ornaments the crest and is repeated on the skirt and knees.

86 Corner Chair

B.58.107

New York, 1760–1780
Mahogany, ash. H.31½ W.30½ D.26½

The conservative solid splat with simple piercing and an elongate shell at the knee are features found in other New York examples.[14] Unique to this corner chair, however, is the rich rococo carving across the crest rail. Although related in ornament to side and armchairs belonging to the van Rensselaer family, this rococo detail is considerably less conventional, more fluid, and approaches Philadelphia carving in style.

14. A similar unornamented chair is at Winterthur (Downs, No. 66)

87 Corner Chair

B.69.401

New York, 1760–1790
Mahogany, pine. H.32 W.32¼ D.26¼

A comparatively large number of New York corner chairs survive today, suggesting a predilection there for that form. This example with its heavy scrolled splat, flattened ball feet and leaf carving at the knee matches a side chair belonging to Philip Schuyler (1737–1804) and was originally part of the same set.[15]

15. Rice, p. 43.

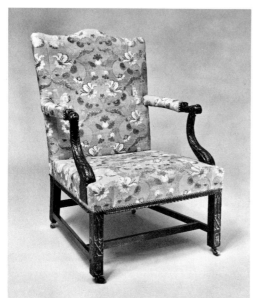

88   Armchair   B.60.33

Massachusetts, 1760–1790
Mahogany, maple. H. 44½ W. 26½ D. 30

Upholstered high-back chairs with open wooden arms were favored in Rhode Island and Massachusetts in the late eighteenth century. The example here, with double-kinked or s-shaped arms, relates to a small group of Massachusetts chairs which have been associated with the Newburyport cabinetmaker, Joseph Short (1771–1819).[16] The arms and profile of the legs are not unlike those of No. 83.

16. *Antiques*, April 1945, p. 222. Similar chairs are at Winterthur (Downs, No. 58); Museum of Fine Arts, Boston (Hipkiss, No. 81); a private collection (Biddle, No. 38).

89   Armchair   B.60.30

Thomas Affleck, active 1763–1795
Philadelphia, 1765–1775
Mahogany, oak. H. 39¾ W. 28½ D. 30½

Chippendale's *Director*, Plate XIX, served as the model for a group of upholstered armchairs made in Philadelphia.[17] Stylistically, they have been attributed to Thomas Affleck (1740–1795), who owned a copy of the *Director*. All have straight, Marlborough legs and are ornamented with the richest of Philadelphia carving. This example combines the three tastes of Chippendale: Gothic and Chinese fretwork on the legs and rococo leaves on the arms. Identical fretwork is known in two other examples.[18] The legs originally were slightly longer, those in the front terminating in block feet. The castors are a replacement.

17. Related examples are at Winterthur (Downs, No. 57); Colonial Williamsburg (Comstock, No. 253); the Philadelphia Museum.
18. This chair is illustrated as Pl. 285 in Hornor; Pl. 117 is nearly identical; a third example is at Winterthur (*Antiques*, December 1970, p. 907).

90   Easy Chair (*opposite*)   B.60.89

Massachusetts, 1760–1790
Mahogany, maple. H. 45½ W. 32 D. 32¼

Although easy chairs were common in the Chippendale period, few have survived with their original upholstery intact.[19] The bright reds and yellows of this eighteenth century bargello, or flame-stitch, attest to a contemporary American taste for strong color. In addition to the original upholstery, the back is covered with original watered, rolled and stamped harateen.[20] The chair also reveals the sleek lines and economy of padding used in upholstery at that time.

19. Three other examples are known: at the Metropolitan Museum, New York (*Antiques*, December 1971, p. 884); the Brooklyn Museum (Schwartz, Fig. 23); Winterthur (Downs, No. 73).
20. Fragments of a nearly identical material are in the Essex Institute, Salem.

51

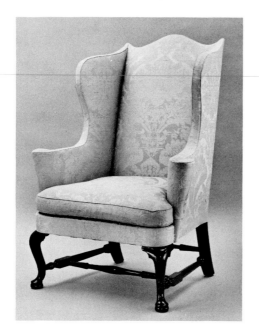

91   Easy Chair   B.69.219
      Massachusetts, 1760–1790
      Mahogany, maple. H. 47 W. 37¼ D. 34

      While the full Chippendale form with serpentine crest
is exemplified here, the pad-like feet evoke the image of an
earlier style. In actuality, however, feet of this type were a
simpler but contemporary variant to the ball and claw. A related example is in the Museum of Fine Arts, Boston.[21]
      21. Randall, No. 154.

92   Easy Chair   B.60.84
      Newport, Rhode Island, 1770–1790
      Mahogany, maple, pine. H. 48 W. 36 D. 29

      Straight legs, introduced in reaction to the cabriole,
gained popularity during the 1770's. While these legs were
often ornamented with fretwork of Chinese inspiration, Newport taste favored fluted legs with the lower fluting filled, a
classical architectural treatment sometimes called stop-fluting,
but properly termed cabled. Thin compact wings lend further
distinction to this example.[22]
      22. For related chairs, see *Rhode Island Furniture*, No. 26; Biddle, No. 40.

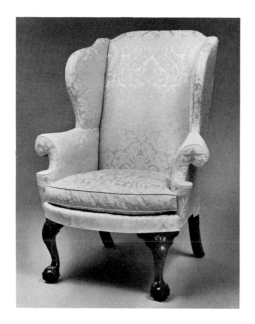

93   Easy Chair   B.69.31
      Philadelphia, 1760–1780
      Mahogany, oak, cherry, pine. H. 46¼ W. 37¼ D. 32¼

      In Philadelphia, the horizontally rolled arm with accom-
panying c-scrolls of the William and Mary form was retained
through the Chippendale period. Indeed, differentiation between Queen Anne and Chippendale expressions of the easy
chair is not always possible. Here, typical Philadelphia shells on
the knees, ball and claw feet and stump rear legs are details
common to both late Queen Anne and Chippendale chairs
(No. 85).

94 Chair-back Settee

B.69.361

Massachusetts, probably Boston, 1760–1790
Mahogany, maple. H. 39 W. 74 D. 27

Although it was a reasonably popular form in England and Ireland, American chair-back settees are extremely rare. Curiously, with four exceptions, known examples have Massachusetts origins.[23] This settee — basically two expanded armchairs with the inner arms omitted — closely conforms to the norm of Massachusetts chairs. It has eight matching side chairs (No. 74). Probably made in Boston, the set descended in the Forbes family of Massachusetts.

23. A closely related settee with matching chairs was exhibited at the Museum of Fine Arts, Boston (*A Bit of Vanity*, Boston, Museum of Fine Arts, 1972, No. 31); one similar, but with three versus four front legs, is illustrated (Sack, *Opportunities*, Number Eighteen, January 1970, No. 1410); another is at Winterthur; an example with matching side chairs is in a private Massachusetts collection. A late example has straight legs (Sack, *Opportunities*, Number One, 1956, No. 37); a Connecticut settee is known (*Antiques*, February 1971, p. 205); a Philadelphia example is illustrated (Hornor, Pl. 240); a New York version is known (Bishop, No. 171); an attributed Charleston, South Carolina, settee is illustrated (*Antiques*, April 1970, p. 578).

95 Settee

B.69.142

Massachusetts or New York, 1755–1770
Mahogany, ash, cherry, pine. H. 32 W. 55½ D. 26½

In the first quarter of the eighteenth century upholstered settees, accommodating two persons, began to appear in American furniture. However, the form was never common and a small cabriole leg example is quite rare. The shaped terminals of the back legs, an English feature, occasionally occurred in New York examples, and the secondary woods suggest a New York provenance. However, the large feet with retracted claw are a Massachusetts type. The rather conservative sweep of the arms and the serpentine back, in contrast to the bold legs, suggest that this is an early attempt at the form.[24]

24. Other more fully developed Massachusetts examples are at Winterthur (Downs, No. 270); the Metropolitan Museum, New York (Comstock, No. 246).

96 Sofa

B.59.73

Philadelphia, 1765–1790
Mahogany, poplar, cedar, oak. H. 38½ W. 66¼ D. 34

A small, sophisticated group of Philadelphia sofas conform closely to Plate XXX of the third edition of Chippendale's *Director*. Usually they have Marlborough legs and block feet. The most elaborate of these sofas is the well-known example at Cliveden made by Thomas Affleck for John Penn.[25] This smaller, plainer one follows Chippendale's advice: "part of the carving may be left out if desired." The serpentine seat rail is an unusual feature.[26]

25. Hornor, Pl. 258.
26. This sofa is illustrated (Hornor, Pl. 202); a closely related example is at Winterthur (Downs, No. 274); a slightly larger four-legged example is at Colonial Williamsburg (Comstock, No. 348).

97   Stand

B.59.33

Massachusetts, 1760–1790
Mahogany, maple. H. 27 DIAM. 23⅞

This small tripod stand with piecrust top has been carefully enriched with carved detail. The vase-shape stem, spirally fluted with a fluted column above, was a composition favored in New England, particularly in Massachusetts.

98   Stand

B.69.103

Probably Newport, Rhode Island, 1760–1790
Mahogany, maple. H. 26¾ DIAM. 16

While the fluted spiral vase motif occurs elsewhere in New England, other details of this stand suggest a Newport origin. The plain, round top is deeply dished, and the feet have long thin bony claws grasping an ovoid ball.[27] Unidentified initials *J.C.S.* are branded under the top.

27. *Rhode Island Furniture*, No. 33.

99   Stand

B.58.144

New York State, 1760–1790
Cherry. H. 26½ DIAM. 19

The robust proportions of this small stand lend a quality of monumentality characteristic of New York furniture. The bold baluster with wide ring above and below, large well-defined snake feet and shells at the knees are attractive features which appear on several other New York examples.[28]

28. Rice, pp. 18, 42.

100 Stand   B.69.360

Philadelphia, 1760–1790
Mahogany. H.29 DIAM.23⅝

This design found great favor for both stands and larger tripod tea tables made in Pennsylvania throughout the Chippendale period. The ball and Tuscan column composition was most common.

101 Stand   B.61.79

Chester County, Pennsylvania, 1760–1800
Walnut. H.23¾ DIAM.16⅝

The pedestal composition is typical of Pennsylvania. Unusual, however, is the round rather than square birdcage with three supports instead of four. Tables with round birdcages are peculiar to Chester County, Pennsylvania, and seem to have been made in the Downingtown area.[29] This table is branded *M.B.* under the top.[30]

29. Schiffer, Pls. 151, 152.

30. Moses Brown of West Caln Township appears as a turner in the 1808 tax assessment (Schiffer, p. 41). Whether there is any connection is not certain.

102 Pole Screen   B.56.5

Philadelphia, 1760–1790
Mahogany, maple. H.59½

The Chippendale pole screen, a new and specialized piece of furniture, was designed to protect one from the heat and glare of the open fire. The lower section, which followed the same design as tea tables and stands, is here enriched with rococo carving. Above, the adjustable screen is covered with contemporary needlepoint and backed with Chinese paper of the same age.

103 Tea Table

B.69.35

Philadelphia, 1760–1790
Mahogany. H. 29 DIAM. 34½

Philadelphia taste preferred round tea tables with tripod bases. The stem, here concealed by the tilted top, conforms to the Philadelphia standard but is without ornament. The tripod base with vigorous stance is richly carved at the knee with naturalistic acanthus. One magnificently figured piece of crotch mahogany forms the piecrust top.

104 Tea Table

B.61.96

Charleston, South Carolina, 1760–1790
Mahogany. H. 27½ DIAM. 28

Although evidence suggests that a considerable amount of furniture was made in eighteenth century Charleston, relatively few examples have been identified. A most unusual detail here is the free-standing c-scroll under each leg, a feature which occurs on another Charleston table in the collection of the Rhode Island Historical Society. The elongate vase, here carved with the same leaves as the legs, is a shape which appears on documented Charleston examples.[31] This table has a history of ownership in the Middleton family.[32]

31. E. Milby Burton, *Charleston Furniture, 1700–1825*, Charleston, South Carolina, The Charleston Museum, 1955, Fig. 130.
32. This table is illustrated in the Middleton home (N. W. Elwell, *Colonial Furniture and Interiors*, Boston, Geo. H. Polley & Co., 1896, Vol. 1, Pl. LX).

105 Tea Table

B.58.108

Newport, Rhode Island, 1755–1780
Mahogany, replaced blocks. H. 26 W. 33½ D. 20½

Rectangular tea tables continued to be made in the Chippendale period. The earlier severe Newport form (No. 60) has been retained, altered only by the addition of ball and claw feet. These are in the finest Newport style with ovoid balls grasped by long knuckled claws. The talons are free standing. The feet and legs are repeated on another Newport tea table and appear on a dressing table also at Bayou Bend (No. 115).[33] The dished top is carved from one solid plank.[34]

33. *Rhode Island Furniture*, No. 30.
34. *Rhode Island Furniture*, No. 31, has the same dished top with indented corners.

106 Tea Table
B.57.1

Newport, Rhode Island, 1760–1780
Mahogany, replaced blocks. H. 26¾ W. 33⅝ D. 19½

This is one of several virtually identical Newport tea tables.[35] Another is the famous Winterthur example made for Jabez Bowen by John Goddard, and on that basis the others have been ascribed to him. Except for the lack of undercut talon, the carved detail of the Bayou Bend table is most closely related to one that descended in the family of Thomas Poynton Ives.[36] This table descended in the family of Elizabeth Ives Bancroft, sister of Thomas Poynton Ives, and undoubtedly the two were made in the same shop.

35. Two are at Winterthur (Downs, Nos. 372–373); one in the collection of Robert Hale Ives Goddard (Carpenter, No. 77); another was in the George B. Lorimer collection and exhibited at the Brooklyn Museum (Schwartz, Pl. XIII); another appears in the background of an oil painting (Carpenter, No. 92).

36. Carpenter, No. 77.

107 Card Table
B.69.88

Newport, Rhode Island, 1760–1785
Mahogany, maple, pine.
H. 27½ W. 34 D. 18½ (closed) 35¾ (open)

Quiet elegance and fine details characterize this example of the Townsend-Goddard school. Use of lustrous, dark "plum pudding" mahogany on a table top is rare. However, the shallow palmette carving on the knees and naturalistic claws with open talons are typical. The combination of claw and pad feet, an English practice, often occurs in Newport examples designed to stand against a wall. Both rear legs are hinged to swing out and give support to the top when open. The surface of the top is plain, lacking pockets for candles or counters. One leaf lifts to reveal a large three-section compartment which could have been used for the storage of cards or silverware. This example relates to other Newport tables ascribed to John Goddard and John Townsend.[37] However, attribution to a specific cabinetmaker within the Townsend-Goddard school is not possible at this time.

37. *Rhode Island Furniture*, No. 34; Downs, No. 348; Carpenter, No. 62; Biddle, No. 69; the Bayou Bend table is illustrated (Carpenter, No. 63).

108 Card Table
B.57.61

Newport, Rhode Island, 1770–1790
Mahogany, maple, pine.
H. 29⅞ W. 32⅞ D. 17 (closed) 34 (open)

This card table, in the Newport expression of the Chinese taste, relates to a breakfast table made by John Townsend.[38] The line inlay at the base of the skirt and in the lower leaf heralds the approaching Federal style.[39]

38. Downs, No. 311.

39. A similar example is illustrated (Carpenter, No. 67).

109 Card Table   B.69.24

New York, 1765–1785
Mahogany, oak, poplar.
H. 26½ W. 34½ D. 17½ (closed) 33½ (open)

One of the most successful forms of American furniture
is the five-leg, serpentine-front New York card table.
Bold gadrooning echoes the horizontal line of the top,
balances its weight, and visually unites the skirt with the
cabriole legs. This table is one of three, within a larger
group of examples, probably produced in the same, as yet
unidentified, shop.[40] Like the others it was fitted with a
small concealed drawer in the inner skirt behind the swing
leg.

40. *Antiques*, May 1973, p. 983.

110 Card Table   B.69.19

Attributed to Thomas Affleck, active 1763–1795
Philadelphia, 1765–1785
Mahogany, poplar, pine, oak.
H. 30 W. 36¾ D. 19½ (closed) 37 (open)

Rich naturalistic carving places this example among the
finest rococo furniture made in Philadelphia. It relates to a
side table at Winterthur with similar carving on the legs[41]
and to a pair of card tables believed to have been made by
Thomas Affleck for Governor John Penn.[42] The latter
tables were sold along with items of Penn furniture at the
famous auction in 1788. This example is branded *HK*
several times on the drawer bottom and runners. Although
the initials may stand for Henry Kepple, who made
purchases at the Penn sale, the table descended in the
family of George Ross (1730–1779). The connection, if
any, between Ross and Kepple is not known.

41. Downs, No. 359.
42. Hornor, Pl. 235.

111 Card Table   B.70.23

Attributed to Thomas Affleck, active 1763–1795
Philadelphia, 1765–1785
Mahogany, oak, poplar.
H. 28 W. 35½ D. 17¼ (closed) 34¾ (open)

In contrast to the curvilinear lines of No. 110, this table
is severely rectangular in the Chinese taste. Carved frets
lend a vaguely oriental flavor, and scrolled brackets
continue that theme. The third motif of the Chippendale
style, the Gothic, is represented by interlaced arches on the
skirt. This treatment is identical to that on the Chew family
sofa which has the same Penn-Chew history as the Bayou
Bend table.[43] It is not certain whether the Chews acquired
these pieces at the time of the 1771 purchase of Governor
John Penn's Philadelphia town house or at the 1788
auction. Nevertheless, on the basis of their Penn
provenance, they have been ascribed to the Governor's
cabinet-maker, Thomas Affleck.

43. Hornor, Pl. 258.

112 Pier Table
B.69.200

New England, possibly Rhode Island, 1780–1800
Mahogany, maple, pine. H. 32½ W. 45¼ D. 22½

This D-shaped side table appears to be a unique form. However, evidence suggests a New England, possibly Rhode Island, origin. The pierced brackets are similar to those on late breakfast and card tables made in Newport (No. 108), and overall it is reminiscent of a more massive pier table made in Rhode Island.[44] The initials *IP*, on the underside of the marble top, could refer to the maker and may be those of Joseph Proud, who worked in Newport.[45] The table descended in the family of Jabez Bowen of Providence.

44. Downs, No. 362.
45. Carpenter, p. 25.

113 Pier Table
B.69.67

Philadelphia, 1755–1790
Mahogany, pine. H. 32 W. 49¾ D. 27

While the classical flame and urn ornament on the skirt of this table suggests the approaching Adamesque neoclassicism, it is more closely allied stylistically to the Palladian finials of the Chippendale period. Leaf ornament projecting through the urn's loop handles is thoroughly rococo in spirit. Pendant husks, *garraya eliptica* — another seemingly neoclassical feature — are carved at the knees, yet similar husks appear on tables of the late Queen Anne style (No. 62). The original top, subsequently replaced, was a black-gray and brown marble called "Egyptian" in eighteenth century Philadelphia.[46]

46. The same type of marble is on a pier table at the Metropolitan Museum, New York (Downs, *Picture Book*, No. 22).

114 Pier Table
B.59.82

Philadelphia, 1760–1790
Mahogany, oak, poplar, pine. H. 29½ W. 49¾ D. 22½

This half-round serpentine table is a vigorous baroque statement overlaid with rococo ornament. Shallow carving along the skirt contrasts with deeply carved acanthus on the legs. The original conforming top is gray Pennsylvania King of Prussia marble. The mate to this example, identical except for a central ruffle with mirror asymmetry, is at the Rhode Island School of Design, Providence.[47]

47. Lockwood, *Pendleton Collection*, Pl. III.

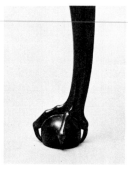

115 Dressing Table   B.59.96
Newport, Rhode Island, 1755–1785
Mahogany, poplar, pine. H.31 W.35¾ D.22

Common in Newport cabinetwork are plain surfaces accented with a raised or recessed shell. Also usual is the practice of horizontally dovetailing the back board onto the stiles. However, the drawer arrangement, which omits the customary single long horizontal drawer in favor of a small central one flanked by enlarged side drawers, is a stylistic departure. Also at variance with the norm is the use of claw feet at the rear. The shell, contained within an arc, is thought to be an early feature. The legs and feet relate to a tea table (No. 105), and the molded top, notched at the corners, is another detail common to both examples.

116 Dressing Table   B.66.15
Philadelphia, 1750–1790
Walnut, poplar, pine. H.36⅝ W.37½ D.20½

This dressing table is transitional from the Queen Anne to the Chippendale styles, the earlier form having been embellished with shells and claw feet (Nos. 85 and 93).

117 Dressing Table   B.69.68
Philadelphia, 1760–1790
Walnut, poplar, pine. H.29 W.36 D.20½

Although the shells and scalloped skirt continue an earlier design, the wide shell-carved central drawer and inset Doric quarter columns are new elements, typical of Philadelphia. Ovolo corners on the molded top are attractive and unusual.

118 Dressing Table

B.69.78

Philadelphia, 1760–1790

Walnut, poplar, pine. H. 29⅝ W. 36 D. 20½

Carving at the skirt and on the knees makes this walnut dressing table more fully rococo than the preceding examples. The bottom of the small left-hand drawer has been repeatedly branded *I. MAYBERRY*, whether the name of the owner or maker is unknown.

119 Dressing Table

B.58.147

Philadelphia, 1760–1790

Mahogany, poplar, pine. H. 30½ W. 34½ D. 20

Three-dimensional carving on the drawer and skirt place this example among the finest of Philadelphia dressing tables. Shallow leafage along the skirt accents the deepness of the central *rocaille* ornament. The inset top and framing molding are uncommon. This dressing table descended in the Longstreth family of Philadelphia.

120 Dressing Table

B.69.527

Maryland, 1765–1790

Mahogany, poplar, pine. H. 29½ W. 35 D. 19¾

Maryland furniture made before the 1790's has always been rare. Although this dressing table does not differ too widely from examples made in nearby Philadelphia, several features indicate a Maryland provenance. The curves of the cabriole legs are more pronounced than those of Philadelphia, and the three small lower drawers are of nearly equal width. Perhaps most notable and typically Maryland, however, is the deeply scalloped skirt with large pendant shell. Suspended from an inverted husk or bellflower, the concave lobate shell is identical in design to one on a Maryland high chest. In all other aspects, save the quarter columns, that example matches this Bayou Bend dressing table.[48] The claw feet correspond closely with those of another Maryland high chest.[49]

48. *Baltimore Furniture*, No. 124.

49. William Voss Elder, III, *Maryland Queen Anne and Chippendale Furniture of the Eighteenth Century*, The Baltimore Museum, 1968, No. 57.

121   Kneehole Dressing Table   B.69.358

Boston area, 1760–1790
Mahogany, pine, gilt. H.29¾ W.36 D.20⅝

This block-front kneehole dressing table is *en suite* with a chest-on-chest (No. 130). They are the Massachusetts equivalent of a matching Philadelphia high chest and dressing table. Typically Massachusetts are the wide top, shaped to conform to the blocking below, narrow flat blocking and tall bracket feet. The use of large-scale hardware is also characteristic.[50]

50. A similar example is in the Museum of Fine Arts, Boston (Randall, No. 28).

122   Kneehole Dressing Table   B.69.232

Massachusetts, 1755–1785
Maple, pine. H.33¼ W.38 D.18½

An alternative form to the cabriole leg dressing table was the kneehole variety. Introduced in English furniture about 1725, kneehole examples began to appear in America, primarily in New England, about 1750. The drawer edges are molded and project over the drawer opening rather than being framed within a bead. This earlier treatment suggests that, at least in concept, this chest predates No. 121. Curly maple, rarely seen in sophisticated urban furniture has been chosen carefully and used to full visual advantage.

123   Kneehole Dressing Table (*opposite*)   B.69.91

Newport, Rhode Island, 1760–1785
Mahogany, poplar, pine. H.34¾ W.38¼ D.21

This block and shell dressing table, one of several, is similar to a labeled example by Edmund Townsend.[51] However, innumerable minor variations of carved detail on this and the other examples suggest that a number of persons within the Townsend-Goddard cabinetmaking clan were producing pieces of this sort.[52] This particular dressing table is made of figured mahogany which has mellowed to an amber tone. It descended in the Vernon family of Newport and is believed to have been owned by William Vernon (1719–1806), son of the silversmith Samuel Vernon.

51. Hipkiss, No. 38.

52. Among the similar examples are: Downs, No. 175; Carpenter, No. 38; *Antiques*, April 1968, p. 484; Nutting, No. 272; *Antiques*, May 1946, p. 292; Comstock, No. 381; *Antiques*, February 1967, p. 207; Sack, *Opportunities*, Number Twenty-one, May 1972; *Antiques*, September 1972, p. 305; *The Lansdell K. Christie Collection of Notable American Furniture*, New York, Sotheby Parke Bernet, Inc., October 21, 1972, No. 20.

124 High Chest
B.69.89

Newport, Rhode Island, 1755–1785
Mahogany, chestnut, pine. H.81 W.29¼ D.22½

Severe plain lines, applied panels at the spandrels and a bonnet top are characteristic of the Rhode Island high chest. Also common is the use of pad feet at the rear. This example by one of the Townsend-Goddard group is distinguished, however, by undercut claw feet, a concave shell and a complex double-tier finial. The carefully scalloped back board behind the broken pediment is a subtle, attractive feature. In the early manner, the shell is contained within an arc.

125 High Chest
B.69.75

Philadelphia, 1760–1775
Mahogany, poplar, pine, cedar. H.94¾ W.46½ D.25

Although the English, after about 1750, no longer made the high chest on cabriole legs, in America that form continued into the Chippendale period, particularly in Philadelphia. There the basic Queen Anne design was embellished with an overlay of rococo ornament. This example, with straight cornice and latticework above, represents a late variation on the form.[53] Two unusual features are the severe, unadorned skirt and the forward tilting cartouche. The maker of this piece has carefully thought out the composition: three strong horizontals and two highly carved areas. The plain skirt offers no visual competition, and the eye is drawn immediately to the crowning detail. Mahogany has been veneered on the mahogany drawer fronts, the grain carefully chosen and arranged. The use of beaded rather than the overlapped drawer edges is an early instance in Philadelphia work. The high chest was made for Joseph Wharton, who died in 1775. A desk-and-bookcase, also made for Wharton and now at the Henry Ford Museum, Dearborn, has the same pediment, cartouche and Gothic fretwork.[54]

53. Two others are part of the same group: the famous Pompadour high chest, Metropolitan Museum, New York (Downs, *Picture Book*, No. 4); the Howe family chest, Philadelphia (Comstock, No. 312).
54. Comstock, No. 337.

126 Chest of Drawers   B.69.39

Boston, 1750–1785
Mahogany, pine. H.29¾ W.35⅝ D.21⅞

Occasionally Massachusetts blocking assumed a curved profile rather than the flattened square treatment of No. 121. While the general form of this block-front chest is common, the use of ogee-bracket feet with the distinctive square pad below is extremely unusual.[55] This treatment is known on only one other example, undoubtedly from the same shop.[56]

55. For other examples, see Downs, No. 169; *Antiques*, June 1953, p. 505; *Antiques*, January 1968, p. 80.
56. *Antiques*, May 1972, p. 744.

127 Chest of Drawers   B.69.136

Boston or Salem, 1760–1790
Mahogany, pine. H.37½ W.37¼ D.21½

The bombé or kettle-base, which originated in France, found great favor elsewhere on the continent, particularly in Holland. It was, however, uncommon in England and even less so in America. All known American examples have a Massachusetts provenance. Here the sweep of the bombé breaks away from the case at the second drawer, and the drawer sides themselves conform to the curve. The combination of long ogee brackets with a central pendant shell is distinctive. A similar bombé chest at Winterthur has the same shell and bracket motif, and it is repeated on two block-front secretaries of Boston or Salem origin.[57]

57. Downs, No. 166; *Antiques*, January 1968, p. 74; Downs, *Picture Book*, No.2.

128 Chest of Drawers   B.69.26

Connecticut, New London County, 1760–1800
Cherry, pine. H.37½ W.38¾ D.19

This cherry block and shell chest approaches the Newport style. It is one of a Connecticut group made in New London County, all having short cabriole legs with ball and claw feet.[58] The blocking, carried down into the brackets, withers in a series of small scrolls rather than flowing into the foot as on No. 129.

58. Downs, No. 172; Kirk, *Connecticut Furniture*, Nos. 62–63.

129 Chest of Drawers

B.69.32

Connecticut, Norwich or Middletown, 1760–1800
Cherry, pine. H.37 W.37¼ D.20

Although this chest is similar to the Newport style, tall vertical proportions, simplified shells, gadrooning along the skirt and the use of cherry indicate another provenance. The piece is one of a number made in the Norwich or Middletown areas of nearby Connecticut. These chests, all very similar, but with minor variations, are the most successful Connecticut adaptations of the Newport design.[59]

59. Downs, No. 170, is the closest; two others have dished tops and vary in other details (Kirk, *Connecticut Furniture*, No. 64; Sack, *Opportunities*, Number Twenty-three, May 1973, p. 45). The former has a gadrooned rather than shell top to the blocking. The latter omits the gadrooning along the skirt.

130 Chest-on-Chest

B.69.357

Boston area, 1760–1790
Mahogany, pine, gilt. H.91¾ W.42½ D.24½

This chest-on-chest matches a block-front kneehole dressing table (No. 121). However, the blocking here is truncated in its upper extremity. The section above, conforming to Boston area fashion, is architectural with Ionic pilasters and broken-scrolled pediment. The shaped upper drawers, corkscrew finials and carved fan are typical of Massachusetts. While a number of Boston area pieces with gilded shells or fans exist, the occurrence here of original gilding on the pilasters, cornice moldings and finials is extremely rare.[60] Although there is a superficial resemblance to a chest-on-chest bearing the label of Benjamin Frothingham, this example has more vertical proportions and varies in many details.[61] Any similarities result from regional traits rather than manufacture in the same workshop.

60. See No. 137 for a Connecticut example.

61. *Antiques*, November 1952, p. 386; other related examples are in the Museum of Fine Arts, Boston (Randall, Nos. 40–41); the Henry Ford Museum, Dearborn (Comstock, No. 304).

131 Chest-on-Chest
B.69.74

Philadelphia, 1760–1790
Mahogany, poplar, pine. H.93 W.47 D.23

The chest-on-chest offered very little opportunity for decoration save the cornice and pediment. Most Philadelphia examples have a straight molded cornice with lattice and scrolled pediment above. Stylistically the treatment here, with central draped plinth, is not unlike the Pompadour high chest.[62]

Three types of cartouches were popular in Philadelphia: interlaced scrolls (No. 125), carved busts or baskets of flowers and leaves. While frets of the type called "Gothick" by Chippendale were most often used, this example is ornamented with interlaced c- and s-scrolls that repeatedly form the letter A. The fine rococo fire-gilded handles and escutcheons are original. Although this example relates to the chest-on-chest made for David Deshler by Thomas Affleck, it differs from that piece by the omission of three small top drawers in favor of an extra, large horizontal one.[63] The proportions too are less vertical than the Deshler chest, suggesting that an attribution to Affleck is not justified. This example can safely be placed, however, on a par with other Philadelphia examples such as the Howe family and Pompadour high chests and thus represents the highest expression of Philadelphia Chippendale cabinetmaking.

62. Downs, *Picture Book*, No. 4.
63. Hornor, Pl. 123.

132 Desk
B.69.225

New England, 1770–1800
Maple, pine. H.40¾ W.34 D.17¼

A number of details found on the interiors of early desks have been incorporated into this example. In addition to a well in the cabinet section, central falling door and projecting outer sections, the slant lid is crossbanded around the edge and ornamented with a "mariner" star, common in New England William and Mary or Queen Anne examples. However, the simple original bail handles together with the use of maple and pine are commensurate with a later date. Despite, the early features this desk must have been made well into the Chippendale period.

133 Desk and Bookcase   B.69.363
Boston area, possibly Braintree or Quincy, 1755–1785
Mahogany, pine. H.97½ W.45 D.23

The drawer sides of this bombé example are straight and do not conform to the swell of the case. Above, the bookcase section with Corinthian pilasters and rococo pediment ornament is very similar to that of a desk, now at Winterthur, which belonged to the Quincy family.[64] The interiors of the bookcase sections are identical, and the small central drawer in the desk section of the Bayou Bend example is a plain version of that on the Quincy desk. An unusual feature is the use of dust boards to separate the lower drawers.[65]

64. Downs, No. 266; for another related example, see Davidson, p. 220.
65. In the early nineteenth century a small upper drawer was inscribed: *This desk was in the possession of I   S E   ng Esquire father to the wife of Benjamin Austin, Esquire for thirty years and then in the possession of said Austin for a number of years.* Benjamin Austin, Jr., married Jane Ivers in Boston in 1785. Presumably, the desk belonged to her father, although it is the first word of the inscription that appears to be Ivers.

134 Desk and Bookcase   B.69.139
Boston, 1765–1785
Mahogany, Pine. H.93 W.40 D.21½

Both bombé and serpentine construction are combined in this small desk and bookcase. The triangular dentiled pediment, later in concept than the swan's-neck treatment of No. 133, follows Chippendale's Plate CVII. This desk descended in the family of Thomas Dawes of Boston (1731–1809), and an eighteenth century chalk inscription *T D* and *T Dawes* written on the back of the bookcase offers conclusive proof of original ownership.[66]

66. This example has been incorrectly published as belonging to William Greenleaf (Comstock, No. 329; *Antiques*, December 1966, p. 800). However, another bombé example in the Whaling Museum, New Bedford, Massachusetts, did belong to Greenleaf and eventually descended in the same family as the Bayou Bend example (*Antiques*, October 1954, p. 237). The finial, mirror, glass and drawer brasses here are replacements.

135 Desk and Bookcase

B.69.22

Newport, Rhode Island, 1760–1785
Mahogany, chestnut, cedar, pine. H.99 W.42¼ D.26½

Newport block and shell secretaries stand among the highest and most innovative expressions of American cabinet-making. Although there are about a dozen known today, each varies slightly; all but three have closed bonnet tops. This one is most closely related in design and proportion to examples at Winterthur and in the Metropolitan Museum, New York, and shares with them double applied panels in the spandrels.[67] The short, fluted finials and cable-fluted quarter columns are on other Newport case pieces.

67. Downs, No. 232; Downs, *Picture Book*, No. 3; other related examples are at the Museum of Fine Arts, Boston (Hipkiss, No. 19; Randall, No. 62); Museum of Art, Rhode Island School of Design (Lockwood, *Pendleton Collection*, p. 232); Yale University, the Garvan Collection (Kirk, *Early American Furniture*, p. 19); The Rhode Island Historical Society (*Rhode Island Furniture*, Fig. 10); the collection of Mrs. Arthur Lisle (Carpenter, No. 43); the collection of John Nicholas Brown, Providence; another private Providence collection.

136 Tall Clock

B.59.83

Works by Edward Spalding of Providence,
    active ca. 1750–1780
Newport, Rhode Island, 1760–1780
Mahogany, pine. H.100¾ W.21½ D.11¾

After the middle of the eighteenth century tall clocks were common. This example, with arched hood in an early style, has fluted cup-shape finials, blocking and the bold lobate shell typical of Rhode Island.[68] A separate piece of light-colored mahogany has been used to make the shell stand out against the darker blocking below.

68. A similar clock is at Winterthur (Downs, No. 205); a second, *Antiques*, August 1968, p. 147; also Carpenter, No. 30; *Antiques*, April 1968, p. 485. A number of shell and block-front Newport tall clocks with a broken-scrolled pediment are also known.

137 Tall Clock

B.60.48

Works by Nathan Howell, active 1741–1784
New Haven, Connecticut, 1760–1784
Cherry, pine. H.91 W.20 D.11¼

Broken-scrolled pediments followed arched hoods in the development of clock design. The rosettes and line of the pediment here are similar to those of a Connecticut high chest.[69] Gilding delineates the finials, rosettes, bases and capitals of the columns and the molding under the hood.[70]

69. Kirk, *Connecticut Furniture*, No. 89.

70. Another example with works by Howell is in the New Haven Colony Historical Society (Brooks Palmer, *The Book of American Clocks*, New York, Macmillan, 1950, p. 215).

138 Bed B.69.137

Massachusetts, 1760–1780
Mahogany, maple. H.86 W.59¾ L.81

The footposts of this bed have been made of mahogany and enriched with fluting, cabriole legs and claw feet. However, in the areas not exposed to view — the headposts and headboard — the maker has economized, using unadorned members made of maple, stained to resemble mahogany. A similar bed is at Winterthur.[71] During the eighteenth century window curtains and bed hangings followed similar designs. The red moreen hangings here are patterned on some in the Brush-Everhard House in Colonial Williamsburg.[72] The bed cover is a circa 1750 Indian painted cotton palampore.

71. Downs, No. 4.
72. Winchester, opposite p. 72.

The Federal Period 1780-1810

The early years of the new Republic marked the first phase of an enthusiasm for the classic past that dominated American taste until the middle of the nineteenth century. The young nation strongly identified with ancient Republican Rome. Officers of the Revolutionary Army organized an hereditary society, The Order of the Cincinnati, tacitly equating their leader, George Washington, with Cincinnatus, the honorable Roman farmer and general. The intellectual climate in America was favorable for establishing a classical tradition.

Seeds of the new style reached Philadelphia as early as the 1770's. An important silver urn made by Richard Humphreys and presented in 1774 by the Continental Congress to its secretary, Charles Thomson, is in the neoclassical taste. Similarly, the writing box made by Benjamin Randolph for Thomas Jefferson and used by Jefferson in drafting the Declaration of Independence incorporated inlaid ornament in the new style. Nevertheless, during the Revolution, interruption of communication between the colonies and London, America's fashion center, delayed thorough introduction and acceptance of new ideas until the 1780's.

Basically, the neoclassical style was the mode which the designer-architect Robert Adam (1728–1792) formulated in Italy, promulgated in England, and published in *Works of Architecture* (1773–1779). Adam drew inspiration from the romantic ruins in Rome, Pompeii and Spoleto and made extensive use of classical motifs which were reinterpreted and combined in a very personal style.

The Adamesque, the accepted London mode by the 1770's, found its way across the Atlantic primarily via printed sources, such as Thomas Shearer, *Designs for Household Furniture* (1788), George Hepplewhite, *The Cabinet-Maker and Upholsterer's Guide* (1788), and Thomas Sheraton, *The Cabinet-Maker and Upholsterer's Drawing Book* (1793). Indeed, the names Hepplewhite and Sheraton have often been used to describe furniture of this period, but the similarity of designs in both publications make distinction between the two virtually impossible. The term Federal is therefore more appropriate for this furniture, made in America.

Although the designs of Adam made a sharp break with the past, his approach toward the classic was distinctly non-archaeological, whimsical and, in spirit, closely related to the rococo. Generally, the furniture of this period was light and delicate. Geometrical shapes and flat surfaces replaced the sinuous lines of the rococo. Straight, often tapering, legs superseded the ubiquitous cabriole.

Classical motifs—vases, swags of drapery and flowers—were reinterpreted and used in a non-classical manner. Contrasting colors and contrasting shapes such as ovals within rectangles were important decorative schemes.

New forms of furniture included specialized pieces designed for use by ladies: worktables (No. 161) and desks (No. 168). During the Federal period the dining room assumed significant importance to American interiors for the first time. In response, furniture intended for use there, specifically the banquet-sized dining table and sideboard (No. 164), was introduced.

American craftsmen quickly adopted the designs of Hepplewhite and Sheraton, occasionally following them rather closely (No. 139), but more often reinterpreting and rearranging the motifs, giving a distinctly American and regional flavor.

In addition to the pre-Revolutionary seaboard centers, Salem and Baltimore, newly wealthy from maritime trade, emerged as producers of extremely fine furniture.

THE DINING ROOM.   Pale, creamy, flowering dogwood painted over gold leaf-covered canvas hangs on the Dining Room walls. This ornament was specially designed and painted for the room by William McKay when the house was built in 1927. The pale green ceiling, cupboard and the white ceiling plasterwork beading are in the Adam style. The English pedestal-base dining table was used here during the years in which Bayou Bend was a private residence. On the table and in the cupboard are pieces of green and gold creamware, which was recently identified as being Spode. White saltglaze stoneware also appears in the cupboard. The lyre, an Adamesque motif, is the major component of the Sheffield plate epergne and candlesticks. The glass tableware is either Irish or English while the chandelier is of English origin. A Chinese export porcelain garniture stands on the mantel.

THE McINTIRE BEDROOM. Furniture from the Boston–Salem–Portsmouth area is found in the McIntire Bedroom. The room takes its name from the pair of chairs at the foot of the bed and several other pieces which were carved by the Salem master carver, Samuel McIntire (1757–1811). Following the Adamesque taste for light colors, the walls are painted pastel blue. The bed hangings and curtains echo the beige tones of the three fine Kulah carpets on the floor. The swag and tassel design of the tester and window pelmets is based on a sketch by Thomas Jefferson. The same motifs appear in the carved ornament of the bed posts.

THE FEDERAL PARLOR. Pale yellow walls, Wedgwood-blue swag draperies and small-scale pastel upholstery reflect the lighter, more feminine, character of Federal period interiors. The mantel, dating about 1800, was used in a house on Second Street, Philadelphia. It is embellished with plaster decoration in the neoclassical taste: bowknots, swags of flowers and vaguely classical maidens. It was probably made in Robert Wellford's American Manufactory of Composition Ornaments.[1] The acorn-finial brass andirons are also from Philadelphia and patriotically bear the great seal of the United States, engraved on the columnar shaft. That spirit of patriotism and enthusiasm for the new nation is reflected in the French gilt-bronze clock inscribed, *Washington First in Peace, First in War and in his Countrymen Hearts'*. Pastel portraits of John Adams and Thomas Jefferson hang on either side.

1. Wellford, the leading manufacturer of ornamental plasterwork, is listed in the Philadelphia *Directories* from 1801 to 1839.

THE MUSIC ROOM.   The maritime prosperity of Federal New England is reflected in this room. French panoramic wallpaper, Dufour et LeRoy's *Banks of the Bosporus*, ornaments the walls. A Chinese export porcelain tea service with sepia eagle decoration is set out on the small tables. A mantel designed by Samuel McIntire for Salem's Registry of Deeds served as a model for this one.[2] An American eagle ornaments the tablet. A lyre-base New York piano gives the room its name.

   2. The original is now in the Essex Institute, Salem (Kimball, Fig. 216).

139 Side Chair (one of a pair)   B.61.92

Carved by Samuel McIntire, 1757–1811
Salem, Massachusetts, 1790–1800
Mahogany, ebony, ash, maple. H. 38 W. 32 D. 20

This chair was carved by Samuel McIntire for Elias
Hasket Derby of Salem. The design is based on Plate 2 of
Hepplewhite's *Guide*, but the chairmaker has made slight alterations by adding the spade feet of applied ebony and molding
the stiles and frame of the back. McIntire's carved grape ornament on the splats, at the base of the back and on the legs is an
embellishment of the original Hepplewhite design. The distinctive grape and grape-leaf motifs seem to have been specially
made for the Derby family. These particular chairs belonged
to a large set, examples of which are in the Museum of Fine
Arts, Boston; Winterthur; the Metropolitan Museum, New
York; and the Cleveland Museum.[3]

3. Hipkiss, No. 91; Montgomery, No. 14.

140 Side Chair (one of a pair)   B.69.378

Boston or Salem, 1790–1795
Mahogany, birch, maple. H. 38½ W. 21 D. 19¾

Inlaid patera, a lunette at the base of the shield back and
a shallow-carved basket of fruit with trailing vines are all distinctive features of this pair of chairs. While the carved ornament repeats motifs often found in the most outstanding Salem
furniture, it is interesting to note that this chair, and one virtually identical, have Boston family histories.[4] A third chair of
related but far simpler design has been ascribed to William
Fiske (1770–1844) who worked in Salem until about 1800.[5]
That chair has a documented history of having been owned by
John Hancock. Although an attribution to Fiske is tentative at
best, there exists a strong possibility that this pair is of Boston,
rather than Salem, origin.

4. The Bayou Bend pair has a history of ownership by Major Thomas
Melville (1751–1832); a second example is in the Museum of Fine Arts,
Boston (Hipkiss, No. 93); a third at Winterthur (Montgomery, No. 33).
Another piece of furniture owned by Melville is known (Randall, No.
28, "Notes").

5. Randall, No. 128.

141 Side Chair (one of a pair)   B.66.11

John Townsend, 1732–1809
Newport, Rhode Island, 1800
Mahogany, maple. H. 38 W. 21½ D. 19½

Documented Federal style furniture made in Newport
is exceedingly rare. Indeed, the design of the back, the flared
front legs and horizontal braces extending from front to back
of the seat are all features more often found in New York
examples of this period. However, a hand-written label pasted
inside the rear seat rail (see detail) states that these chairs and
their mates were made by John Townsend, Newport, 1800.[6]
Fine punchwork around the patera, delicate beading on the
splats and legs and overall excellence of design attest that Townsend remained a master into the Federal period.

6. A matching chair is at Winterthur and a fourth in the collection of
Joseph K. Ott (*Antiques*, September 1968, p. 388).

142 Side Chair (one of a pair)   B.57.70

Attributed to John and Thomas Seymour,
    active ca. 1794–1810
Boston, ca. 1805
Mahogany, birch, maple. H.35 W.18¾ D.19¾

This side chair is one of a sophisticated group attributed to the shop of John and Thomas Seymour.[7] All have similar square, scrolled backs with veneered tablet and out-turned veneered legs, as here, or turned and reeded legs. Rich contrasting panels on the tablet and legs are in the best Adamesque tradition and were a treatment favored in the Boston-Salem-Newburyport-Portsmouth area (No. 155 and No. 167). The scrolled back and sabre-shaped front legs anticipated the klysmos form of the Empire style.

7. The Museum of Fine Arts, Boston, has a pair (Hipkiss, No. 116); a matching pair is at Winterthur (Montgomery, No. 38). The Bayou Bend examples are slightly simpler, having a plain mahogany seat rail, and more nearly match a pair at the Henry Ford Museum, Dearborn (Stoneman, *Supplement*, No. 57).

143 Side Chair (one of four)   B.64.9.3

New York, ca. 1800
Mahogany, ash, pine. H.35¾ W.21½ D.19½

The square back of this side chair is based on Plate 36, No. 2, of Sheraton's *Drawing Book*. In the Adamesque manner, motifs of classical origins have been playfully combined: the back is intersected by a columned arch, and an urn with drapery forms the splat. This pattern found especial favor with New York cabinetmakers, and many similar examples made there have survived.[8] Typically, the prototype has been simplified, with three instead of four vertical members in the vase, and altered by piercing the vase and adding a fluted tablet across its top. Reeded front legs with spade feet were the New York norm for this sort of chair.

8. At Winterthur (Montgomery, Nos. 58–60); at the Museum of Fine Arts, Boston (Hipkiss, Nos. 107–108).

144 Armchair (one of a pair with six   B.60.37
    matching side chairs)

Attributed to Duncan Phyfe, 1768–1854
New York, ca. 1800
Mahogany, ash, pine. H.37½ W.18 D.20¼

Although the initial appearance of this example seems to be identical to No. 143, it varies in a number of subtle details. The urn-shape splat is larger and has four vertical members following the Sheraton design. However, diverging from the prototype, carved leaves are substituted for the Prince-of-Wales feathers, and the drapery clings to the side of the urn rather than hanging free. The stiles and crest are reeded, and the front legs, inset with concave panels, terminate in rather blunt spade feet. This chair is slightly larger than usual, a fact that suggests, as does the finesse of detail, that the whole set was originally both special and expensive.

The chairs descended in the family of Emily Phyfe Dunham, a great-niece of Duncan Phyfe. It is likely that the set represents the earliest phase of Phyfe's New York work.

145 Armchair (one of a pair) 69.375

New York, 1790–1800
Mahogany, ash. H. 39¼ W. 21½ D. 19¾

A combination of the shield back and double-festooned drapery was favored in New York. Other features such as the leaf-carved lunette at the base of the shield, the pointed leaves at the juncture of the arms and stiles and the small plinths at the base of the arms are all details found in many New York examples. The reeded legs and spade feet are not unlike No. 143. In design, the back is a variant that appears on two very similar New York chairs at the Museum of Fine Arts, Boston.[9]

9. Hipkiss, Nos. 94–95.

146 Armchair (one of a pair) B.61.43

Philadelphia, 1790–1800
Poplar, mahogany, pine. H. 37½ W. 24 D. 22

Painted furniture found great favor in the designs of Robert Adam, and both Hepplewhite and Sheraton, describing the plates in their books, often wrote that chairs were to be finished in white and gold or japanned. Strangely, with the exception of Baltimore where it was fairly common, American painted furniture of the early Federal period occurs only in isolated instances. This Philadelphia example is painted pale yellow and decorated with pastel blue ornament — bowknots, husks and swags in the best Adamesque tradition. Mahogany arms, a practical but slightly incongruous touch, are not without precedent, occurring in some of the most sophisticated Philadelphia Windsor furniture.[10] This pair of chairs belonged to the Chew family. Matching examples remain today at Cliveden.[11]

10. Hornor, Pls. 473, 502.
11. Hornor, Pl. 430.

147 Lolling Chair B.69.369

Massachusetts, 1795–1805
Mahogany, maple. H. 44½ W. 26 D. 27½

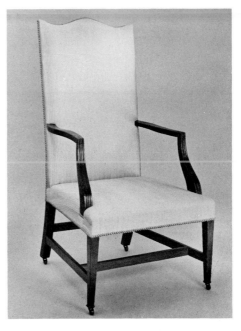

A mutation of the upholstered high-back, open armchairs of the earlier eighteenth century, the Federal style Martha Washington or lolling chair, seems to be a distinctly American form without parallel in English furniture. This type of chair appears to have occurred only in New England, where it was fairly common. Distinguished details of this example include the fine molding of the arm supports, carefully blended into the arms themselves, and the crisply peaked serpentine top of the back. As with most early lolling chairs, the arms are set back and attached to the frame rather than being attached to, or a continuation of, the front legs, as in No. 148.

148 Lolling Chair

B.69.128

Portsmouth, New Hampshire, 1800–1810
Mahogany, birch. H.45 W.26 D.28½

Extraordinary beauty and grace distinguish this interpretation of the lolling chair. Delicately turned legs flow up across the seat frame and into the arm supports, which continue onward into the light sinuous arms. The transition between circular and rectangular section is both subtle and successful. Flared corners at the top of the serpentine back echo the lines of the arms, and satinwood panels ornament the seat rail passage. Although published as the work of the Seymours,[12] this chair is closely allied with a body of Portsmouth, New Hampshire, pieces and resembles a pair owned by Portsmouth silversmith William Simmes (1775–1824).[13] It is likely that it was made there.

12. Stoneman, No. 218.
13. *Antiques*, August 1922, p. 50; Comstock, No. 438; Montgomery, Nos. 271–272.

149 Easy Chair

B.60.93

Baltimore, Maryland, 1790–1800
Mahogany, ash, poplar. H.50 W.35½ D.31¾

From its introduction in the early eighteenth century the easy chair varied little in basic construction. Only the supporting members were changed in accord with the prevailing fashion. However, during the last quarter of the eighteenth century the structure of the upholstered frame was altered by placing the wings on top of the arms rather than attaching the arms to wings that continued down into the seat. The general design appears in Plate 15 of Hepplewhite's *Guide*. Overall, the Federal easy chair is considerably lighter and thinner than its predecessors. This example is distinguished by its serpentine skirt and tapering inlaid legs, which conform to the serpentine line, the sharply canted back and flaring, downward-raked arms. This latter feature occurs in Federal easy chairs of Baltimore provenance.

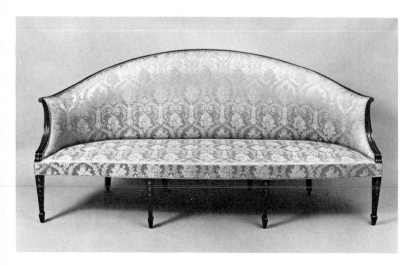

150 Cabriole Sofa

B.61.13

New York, ca. 1800
Mahogany, ash, maple. H.38⅝ L.84 D.26

Exposure of the frame in a continuous arm and back composition was a major innovation in Federal period sofas. This example with curvilinear arms and arched back is a type contemporarily referred to as "cabriole." While similar sofas were made in Baltimore, inclusion of an outward flare and inlaid rosette (visually breaking the flow of line) at the juncture of the arms and back, indicates a New York origin.[14] Inlaid rosettes often occur on New York armchairs, and the inlaid husks on the tapering spade-footed legs also conform to New York design.

14. A closely related example is at Winterthur (Montgomery, No. 265); another square-back New York sofa has a similar arm treatment (Comstock, No. 529).

151 Square-Back Sofa   B.56.172
Carved by Samuel McIntire, 1757–1811
Salem, Massachusetts, ca. 1800–1810
Mahogany, birch. H. 35 L. 71½ D. 29¾

Free-standing arm supports connecting the seat rail and arm are a late innovation of Federal sofa design that seems to have come from Sheraton's works. Plate 35 of Sheraton's *Drawing Book* was the inspiration for a group of Salem sofas which incorporate that feature along with rather distinctive carving. While the names of at least two cabinetmakers have been associated with sofas of this type, they all are decorated with stylized carving, either by Samuel McIntire or someone working in his mode. Usually, the central tablet of the top rail is ornamented with a latticework basket, filled with fruit and flanked with trailing laurel.[15] The basket appears as an architectural motif in McIntire houses. The leg treatment varies from rectangular to turned, from plain to reeded.

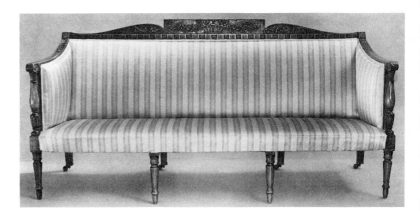

15. Similar examples are at the Museum of Fine Arts, Boston (Hipkiss, Nos. 121–122); at Winterthur (Montgomery, Nos. 269–270); at the Metropolitan Museum, New York; Yale University, the Garvan Collection. For discussion of the carved details, see Fales, *Samuel McIntire*, p. 62.

152 Sofa   B.69.85
New York, 1805–1810
Mahogany, ash, maple. H. 35⅜ L. 78½ D. 30

While at first glance this piece seems to be identical to the New York scroll-back, curved-arm sofas attributed to Duncan Phyfe, several details differ from any known examples. The richly carved tablet, reeded arms, seat rail and legs follow the usual pattern, but the legs are shorter and more bulbous. The vase-shape section of the arm support is less tall than most and is leaf carved rather than reeded. The central panel of the back is carved with crossed, wheat-filled cornucopia, a motif seen on other examples with a Phyfe attribution.[16] However, the other panels are ornamented with fasces, the emblem of ancient Roman magistrates, which is not known to appear on any other New York sofa. Although one is tempted to attribute this example to Phyfe, these differences and the fact that many other cabinetmakers were capable of creating such a sofa, make such an attribution risky.

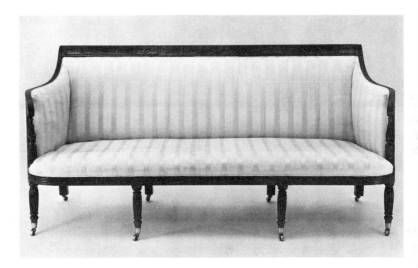

16. Charles O. Cornelius, *Furniture Masterpieces of Duncan Phyfe*, Garden City, New York, Metropolitan Museum of Art, 1922, Pl. XVII; McClelland, p. 163.

153 Card Table   B.69.408
Philadelphia, 1790–1800
Mahogany, pine. H. 29¼ W. 36 D. 17¼ (closed)
                 34⅝ (open)

Delicate tapering legs, lightness of design and rich contrasting inlays are typical of the early Federal period. The ornament, particularly the banding at the skirt, the top edges and the framing of the central panel are in the Philadelphia-Baltimore idiom. However, similar fluted inlay over the legs occurs on a Philadelphia Pembroke table.[17] A related card table at Winterthur is a documented West Chester, Pennsylvania, piece.[18]

17. Hornor, Pl. 395.

18. It was made by Samuel Bellerjeau (active ca. 1823) and bears his stamp. A nearly identical five-legged example is in the Philadelphia Museum (Nutting, No. 1035).

154 Card Table
B.69.129

Baltimore, Maryland, ca. 1795
Mahogany, satinwood, pine, oak.
H. 29½ W. 37 D. 18¼ (closed) 36⅞ (open)

Card tables assumed a variety of forms during the Federal period. Among the most popular early shapes was the circle, a favored motif of Robert Adam. This example is elaborately inlaid on all surfaces, suggesting that it was originally an expensive piece. The vocabulary of ornament, consisting of bellflowers with long central petals, bandings and pictorial inlay of leaves and flowers on the top, indicates a Baltimore provenance.[19]

19. *Baltimore Furniture*, No. 1, illustrates a nearly identical example.

155 Card Table
B.65.9

Boston or Salem, 1805–1810
Mahogany, satinwood, pine, maple.
H. 29 W. 36¼ D. 17¼ (closed) 34¼ (open)

Panels of light wood and elaborate checkered inlay identify the origin of this card table as the Boston-Salem-Newburyport area. Rather distinctive, however, is that the reeding of the legs begins about one-fourth of the way down and terminates at a corresponding distance from the foot. The elongated bulb feet are also unusual. Although both these features appear on tables ascribed to Boston, specifically to the Seymours,[20] there is a shallowness of skirt and resultant legginess of composition that suggest a Salem maker.[21]

20. Stoneman, Nos. 132–133; *Supplement*, No. 40.
21. Montgomery, No. 311.

156 Gaming Table
B.69.377

Salem, Massachusetts, 1805–1810
Mahogany, pine. H. 30¼ W. 26⅝ D. 19⅛

Furniture of the Federal period was often both innovative and specialized. The reversible top of this gaming table, inlaid on one side as a checkerboard, can be removed to reveal a space laid out for backgammon.[22] This area and the drawer interior are painted the distinctive blue, often found on Seymour pieces, but also occurring on a documented Salem desk, by William Appleton (1765–1822), now at Winterthur. In fact, color appears on a number of Boston and Salem pieces.[23] Finely executed leaf carving on the ovolo corners is reminiscent of the treatment found on several pieces by William Hook of Salem (1777–1867),[24] yet the profile of the legs here is quite different, relating much more closely to those of a pair of labeled side tables by William Haskell (1791–1860), also of Salem.[25] An elliptical arch beneath the skirt is a sophisticated and attractive feature. While attribution to a specific cabinetmaker does not seem possible, there is no doubt that this table represents the finest Salem craftsmanship.

22. A table with similar function and sliding top appears in Smith, Pl. 78, and is described there as a "backgammon work table."

23. Randall, No. 65, "Notes".
24. Randall, Nos. 70, 100.
25. Montgomery, No. 343.

157 Gaming Table   B.61.105

Boston, 1800–1810
Mahogany, satinwood, rosewood, ebony.
H. 29½ DIAM. 24¼

A simple design belies the high degree of sophistication on this seemingly unique table. Large areas of contrasting light wood place it in the Boston–Portsmouth corridor. Distinctive details are the pyramidal inlay and rosewood banding around the ebony and maple checkerboard. These in combination with panels of satinwood veneer and an ormolu molding at the base of the stem all relate to examples of the most elaborate Boston work of the first decade of the nineteenth century.[26] Two small drawers (now missing) originally hung from the underside.

26. Montgomery, Nos. 343–344; Hipkiss, No. 30; Stoneman, No. 193.

158 Pole Screen with Shelf   B.61.77

Massachusetts, 1795–1800
Mahogany. H. 57¼

The pole screen, a specialized form introduced during the eighteenth century, has been adapted here to the neoclassical taste, incorporating an urn-shaped pedestal and finial. The screen itself is the favored Adamesque oval. The semicircular folding shelf is an extra feature. This example is embellished by inlaid stringing, outlining the shelf and screen. Pictorial inlaid ovals feature cockleshells from which small beetles emerge, a Massachusetts motif.[27]

27. Montgomery, p. 34, No. 99.

159 Stand   B.69.373

Connecticut, 1785–1810
Cherry, pine. H. 28 W. 16½ D. 16⅛

A classical urn-shaped pedestal and stringing on the top surface place this small utilitarian stand in the Federal period. A narrow drawer, suspended below, is an unusual feature. This drawer, possibly intended for candles, and the turned ring at the neck of the pedestal are on a similar cherry table with elaborate inlay made in Connecticut. It is likely that this example was made there.[28]

28. Montgomery, No. 376.

160 Stand

B.69.127

Rhode Island or Connecticut, 1790–1810
Cherry, pine. H. 25¾ W. 17⅜ D. 17⅝

A profuse amount of effort has been lavished on this small stand. The inlaid ornament, consisting of fans, rope banding and a wavy rayed circle, is elaborate. These details relate closely to a secretary at Winterthur.[29] The naiveté of ornament, combined with the off-beat feature of one real and three blind drawers, suggests a Connecticut provenance. However, similar inlay appears on a Providence desk and bookcase labeled by Webb and Scott.[30] Therefore, a Rhode Island origin is an equally possible attribution.

29. Montgomery, No. 177; another very similar secretary is illustrated in *Frederick K. & Margaret R. Barbour's Furniture Collection*, Hartford, The Connecticut Historical Society, 1963, p. 68. It is inscribed D. Webb, Jr., and may refer to the Providence firm of Webb and Scott (see Note 30).

30. Sale Catalogue of the *Collection of the Late Philip Flayderman*, New York, Anderson Galleries, January 1930, No. 431. The Bayou Bend table has evidence of a label having been on the drawer bottom. Unfortunately, it was removed.

161 Work Table

B.69.383

Salem, Massachusetts, 1805–1810
Mahogany, pine. H. 30¾ W. 20½ D. 15¼

The work table was one of the specialized forms introduced during the Federal period. The top drawer of this example was arranged for writing with an adjustable flap (now missing). The lower drawer was compartmentalized for the storage of thread and other sewing materials. A bag for storage of needlework is suspended from the leading edge of the serpentine skirt. Bold ovolo corners lend extra sophistication. Ogee turning at the top of delicately reeded legs and ring ornament above appear on both Boston and Salem examples. However, distinctive beaded molding around the base of the skirt is a motif with strong Salem associations.[31]

31. Montgomery, No. 405; Randall, No. 70.

162 Work Table

B.61.97

Carved by Samuel Field McIntire, 1780–1815
Salem, Massachusetts, 1810–1815
Mahogany, pine. H. 28½ W. 22¼ D. 19

Heavier proportions and bold carving indicate a later date for this work table. The carved ornament, particularly the canopy of acanthus leaves at the top of the leg, relates to a group of Boston or Salem beds (see No. 171). However, the turning of the lower leg is identical to a Salem example at Winterthur, and the general design echoes that of two Salem work tables.[32] The style of carving is the same as on other pieces assigned to Samuel Field McIntire.[33] The sewing bag is missing.

32. Montgomery, No. 413; Randall, No. 103.
33. Fales, *Essex County Furniture*, No. 63.

163 Cellarette
B.62.23

Virginia or North Carolina, 1800–1810
Cherry, walnut, yellow pine. H.35 W.17 D.14½

The cellarette, literally a small cellar for the storage of wine bottles, seems to be a distinctly southern form; Federal period American examples range from Maryland to Georgia. They characteristically stand on tall legs and are often fitted with a drawer for cutlery. This one is made of cherry with a walnut top. The presence of hard yellow pine further suggests a southern origin while the unsophisticated inlays indicate a non-urban provenance, possibly southern Virginia or northern North Carolina.

164 Sideboard
B.69.199

Salem, Massachusetts, 1795–1805
Mahogany, maple, pine. H.40 L.74 D.28¼

In the architecture of Robert Adam the dining room assumed new importance. One of the furniture forms developed by Adam was the sideboard, which added cupboards and drawers to the traditional sideboard table. Americans of the Federal period readily adopted the innovation. This example, with its serpentine front and recessed central section, represents the earliest type. Not unlike the Adamesque floor plan, it is characterized by undulating mahogany surfaces inlaid in contrasting geometric shapes: circles, ovals and rectangles. Even the hardware has assumed an Adamesque shape, the oval. The tapering legs are canted, conforming to the serpentine line above. Inlaid ornament of bellflowers and husks, alternating with pointed ovals and terminating in three small circles, indicates a Salem origin.

165 Chest of Drawers
B.69.379

Portsmouth, New Hampshire, 1790–1800
Mahogany, birch, pine. H.37 W.40 D.20⅝

In the best Adamesque tradition, contrasting geometric shapes and flat surfaces, broken by the oval hardware, give visual impact to this bow-front chest of drawers. Finely figured crotch birch, with alternate horizontal and vertical grain, is veneered onto the drawer fronts. The central drop panel not only echoes the arrangement of the drawers above, but visually breaks the horizontal sweep of the skirt. French feet, with straight sides and a sharp flare at the base, are seemingly peculiar to Portsmouth.

166 Commode

B.47.3

New York, 1805–1810
Mahogany, pine. H. 44½ W. 48⅝ D. 23¼

This demilune commode is an extremely unusual form.[34] It is veneered with rich, red, highly-figured mahogany. Handsome astragal-ended panels ornament the large cupboard doors at the sides. Reeded legs with small bulbs relate to those used on New York furniture, especially sofas and card tables. This piece is similar to a butler's bureau made by Duncan Phyfe but differs by having a graduated tier of drawers rather than cupboards below the desk area.[35] Another similar New York example is fitted out with an adjustable looking glass in a dressing drawer.[36] The top drawer of this chest is compartmented and has the side braces for an adjustable ratcheted flap. Whether it was intended for a writing surface or looking glass is not known. The hardware has been replaced; originally there were pulls for the side drawers.

34. Hipkiss, Nos. 28, 42 are Massachusetts counterparts; No. 43 is a related form.
35. McClelland, p. 250.
36. *Antiques*, December 1972, p. 941.

167 Gentlemen's Secretary

B.61.94

Salem, Massachusetts, 1795–1800
Mahogany, pine. H. 87¼ W. 70⅝ D. 19⅞

Salem breakfront secretaries found great favor both in local use and as venture cargo. Today a generic term for this form is "Salem secretary." This example, combining desk and secretary functions, exhibits the finest workmanship. Notable are the figured veneers, elaborate patterned inlays and complicated pointed-oval muntins. Interlaced lozenges with stringing on the frieze are a typical Salem motif as are the husk and oval inlay on the stiles. Finely figured ovals, outlined with inlay, are set within mitred panels on the cupboard doors and on the desk lid. While in its general aspect this example relates to the work of Edmund Johnson (active ca. 1793–1811),[37] the treatment of the muntins is closer to a labeled example by Nehemiah Adams (1769–1840). Also, the arrangement and inlay of the desk interior is similar.[38] Attribution therefore to a specific Salem cabinetmaker is not possible at this time. There is, however, firmer ground for attributing the carved eagle finial to Samuel McIntire.[39]

37. In the Henry Ford Museum, Dearborn (Comstock, No. 315); at Winterthur (Montgomery, No. 179).
38. Montgomery, No. 181; Sack, *Opportunities*, Number Seventeen, April 1969, No. 1037; for other related examples, see *Antiques*, May 1933, pp. 168–169.
39. Fales, *Samuel McIntire*, Fig. 46, illustrates a very similar large-size eagle. The finial of a related Salem secretary at the Museum of Fine Arts, Boston, is virtually identical (Randall, No. 67).

168   Tambour Desk   B.65.12

John and Thomas Seymour, active 1794–1804
Boston, Massachusetts, 1794–1804
Mahogany, pine.   H. 41⅜   W. 37½   D. 19½

This lady's desk represents the highest expression of the
Federal period, both in terms of design and craftsmanship. In
all features it is like a group attributed to John and Thomas
Seymour of Boston[40] and is nearly identical to the labeled
example at Winterthur, varying only in minor details and the
use of molded spade feet.[41] Script initials *JS* written in pencil
on the upper surface of the desk (where it is normally covered
by the tambour section) confirm an attribution to John and
Thomas Seymour.

40. Stoneman, No. 14; Hipkiss, No. 29.
41. Montgomery, No. 184.

169 Tall Clock
B.71.52

David Young, active ca. 1775–1815; died 1836
Hopkinton, New Hampshire, ca. 1805–1815
Maple, pine. H.92½ W.21¼ D.11

This tall case clock with rounded hood and open fretwork was a typical form made throughout the Federal period in New England and generically termed "Roxbury." The maple case, stained to look like mahogany, is inlaid with naive stringing, patera and fans in the Federal taste. The case bears the label of *David Young/Joiner/Hopkinton, Newhamp/Shire.*[42]

42. Little is known about David Young's work other than several clocks bearing his label (Randall, *New Hampshire*, No. 87); a labeled chest of drawers is illustrated (*The American Collector*, June 1937, p. 15). Young appears in various Hopkinton records from 1776 until 1823. The author is indebted to Charles S. Parsons of Goffston, New Hampshire, for this information.

170 Wall Clock
B.61.65

Massachusetts, ca. 1813–1815
Mahogany, pine. H.40 W.10½ D.3⅞

The so-called banjo clock is a distinct American innovation. Developed about 1795 by Simon Willard (1753–1848) and patented by him in 1802, these wall clocks, although small, were capable of running for eight days. Typical of the form are the round head, long slender waist, a rectangular base and molded bracket below. The gilded case and gold and white ornament on glass are Adamesque in palette, but the naval engagement on the lower glass pertains to the War of 1812 and indicates that the clock was made about that time.

171 Bed
B.69.393

Boston or Salem, 1800–1810
Mahogany. H.78 W.62 L.77½

During the Federal period, beds became considerably more lavish with larger, highly ornamented posts, elaborate cornices and rich bed hangings. This example, with turned posts in the Sheraton mode, is one of a group made in the Boston-Salem area.[43] Gothic arches, a tasseled canopy of drapery and waterleaves are the ornamental motifs. The same motifs appear in a slightly different order on another example, in the Nelson Gallery, thought to be from Salem.[44] A third bed with virtually identical, though slightly more enriched, carving is in a private Providence collection.[45] It is likely these two and the Bayou Bend bed were made in the same city, if not the same shop, but whether Boston or Salem is not clear.

43. Winterthur (Montgomery, No. 1); *The Metropolitan Museum of Art, Guide to the Collections; The American Wing*, Metropolitan Museum of Art, 1961, No. 65; Museum of Fine Arts, Boston (Randall, No. 214).

44. *Handbook of the Collections in the William Rockhill Nelson Gallery of Art and Mary Atkins Museum of Fine Arts*, Kansas City, Missouri, 1959, p. 163; this same bed or an identical one is illustrated in Nutting, No. 1513.

45. *Rhode Island Furniture*, No. 89. This example is attributed to Providence but the grounds do not seem convincing.

The Empire Period 1810-1830
The Restauration Period 1830-1850

Enthusiasm for the ancient world, born in the Federal era, reached maturity during the Empire period and found its final expression and eventual decline in the Restauration style. Indeed, the classical past gained wide acceptance in the United States in the era before 1850, as Americans built white wooden Grecian temples in towns named Athens, Sparta, Troy and Rome.

The Empire period, or second phase of neoclassical taste, differed from the Adamesque Federal style in its approach, which was much more serious and archaeologically correct. The period takes its name from the Empire of Napoleon I (1810–1815), whose court eagerly adopted classical designs brought to light by archaeological discoveries during the latter part of the eighteenth century. A parallel development occurred almost simultaneously in England as tastes tired of the effete playful classicism of Robert Adam. By about 1810 Americans were adopting the French furniture designs of Charles Percier and Pierre François Fontaine. Somewhat later they were joined by those of Pierre de la Mésengère, together with English designs of Thomas Sheraton, Thomas Hope and George Smith. Rudolph Ackermann's *The Repository of Arts* (1809–1828), a periodical published in London, also served as an important fashion source.

Flowing curved lines of the antique Grecian klysmos or chair were adapted, and the design of seating furniture, as well as beds, closely approached classical prototypes (No. 177). Tables stood on classically inspired bases. In earlier examples, sabre-shape legs were used, only to be replaced with animal paw feet and legs derived directly from antique models. Columns and pilasters were incorporated into tables and case pieces (Nos. 189, 196). Heavier, bolder and more massive proportions succeeded the light delicacy of the Federal taste. Rich dark mahogany veneers were widely employed, often ornamented or accented with classically designed ormolu mounts, brass inlay or painted decoration in imitation of metal (No. 196). In fact, imitative painting reassumed importance in this period, and often surfaces were ebonized or made to resemble antique bronze, verd antique; graining in imitation of rosewood also occurred. Motifs with antique connotations — the eagle, cornucopia and lyre — found great favor.

By about 1825 the carved and ornamented style began to give way to restrained lines and plain surfaces. This simplification of the classical style originated at the French court during the restoration of the Bourbon monarchy after the fall of Napoleon in 1814, hence the term Restauration style. Massive proportions and classically inspired designs were maintained but were reduced to the simplest outline, often rendered in unadorned pillar and scroll form. The designs of George Smith's *Cabinet-Maker & Upholsterer's Guide* (London,

1826) included many examples of the new mode. By 1833 the Restauration style had been assimilated sufficiently for forms in that taste to be included in the famous broadside of Joseph Meeks and Sons, leading New York cabinetmakers. Often considered a debasement of Empire designs, the pillar and scroll style, as it was sometimes called because of its primary components, frequently drew on Roman sources.

This furniture, while simple in outline, is characterized by an extremely high degree of technical know-how and craftsmanship. Plain curved surfaces and handsome ogee moldings were skillfully veneered with beautiful matched mahogany.

The mode had received wide acceptance by 1840 when, in America's first completely illustrated book of furniture styles, John Hall noted, "The Style of the United States is blended with European taste, and a graceful outline and simplicity of parts are depicted in all objects."[1] Ironically, Hall's publication came at the end of the Restauration period as the rococo revival was beginning to appear.

1. John Hall, *The Cabinet Makers Assistant*, Baltimore, 1840.

THE CHILLMAN PARLOR.   The Chillman Parlor and adjacent Foyer were named in honor of the late Dorothy Dawes Chillman, wife of the first director of the Museum of Fine Arts and long-time friend and advisor of Miss Hogg.

Architecturally the rooms reflect the taste of the Greek revival era. The tall windows are framed with marble-white pilasters of the sort published in various builders' handbooks. Grecian anthemia ornament the plaster ceiling medallion and molding. The walls are painted a cool classical gray, while the dominant fabric shade is the rich dark green which found great favor in Napoleonic France. That color is repeated in the circa 1835 New York cornice boards at the window heads. Often fine marble mantels were imported, and the gray example here, incorporating period ormolu mounts, was reproduced from an early nineteenth century French one. On the parquet floor is a rich Aubusson-type needlework carpet of the Restauration period. At the windows heavily fringed curtains are pulled to one side in the "Grecian taste," while anthemia ornament the delicate white mull under-curtains.

Furniture from New York and Philadelphia is reflected in the convex girandole mirror. The gold harp with winged classical figures is English. On a Philadelphia table, Tucker porcelain cups and saucers are set out with a Baltimore tea service by Samuel Kirk and spoons by Hyde and Goodrich of New Orleans. To the left is a "French" secretary of Philadelphia provenance, on loan to the Museum from a private collection.

THE CHILLMAN FOYER. In Greek revival architecture, major chambers were often connected by wide openings. Here, white pilasters with carved lotus capitals flank the doorway to the Chillman Parlor. Furniture from Philadelphia and New York is complemented by classically inspired accessories such as the sconces with ebonized female heads, French gilt-bronze caryatid candelabra and a pair of Tucker porcelain urns. The urns were originally owned by James Peale (1749–1831). Tuckerware, made between 1826 and 1837, was the first commercially successful American porcelain. Other examples appear below on the shelf of the pier table. The large baluster-frame looking glass bears the label of Thomas Natt of Philadelphia (working 1825–1838).

172 Side Chair (one of a pair) B.63.22
New York, 1810–1820
Mahogany, ash. H. 32⅛ W. 18½ D. 23

Flowing lines characteristic of the ancient Grecian kly-mos were successfully adapted to chair design in the second decade of the nineteenth century. In the earlier versions, as here, the tablet is contained between the stiles. Although the approach to the classic is more archaeological than in chairs of the Federal period, the ancient design has been altered by the addition of a stay rail, in this case a magnificent spread eagle with boldly carved leafage.[2]

2. Five identical chairs are at Winterthur (Montgomery, No. 76); another at Yale University, the Garvan Collection (Kirk, *Early American Furniture*, p. 67).

173 Side Chair (one of a pair) B.68.141
New York, 1810–1820
Mahogany, ash, pine. H. 32⅜ W. 19⅛ D. 20½

This example conforms to designs sketched by Duncan Phyfe of what apparently was a popular New York form. Typical are the lyre bannister and paw feet, both of which had antique connotations. Reeding on the seat rail and stiles and waterleaf carving on the upper legs are in the New York style.[3]

3. Related examples are at Winterthur (Montgomery, No. 73); the Metropolitan Museum, New York (*Nineteenth Century America*, No. 27).

174 Side Chair B.72.114
New York, 1810–1820
Mahogany, ash, cherry. H. 32¾ W. 18½ D. 19¼

In most of its particulars the example here conforms to the New York norm of No. 173. Unusual are the crossbanding of the upper legs and the harp bannister, a variant on the classical lyre. Although apparently common enough to have been listed in the New York *Price Book* of 1817, only 7 chairs of this variety are known today.[4]

4. In addition to this chair, there is one at the Metropolitan Museum, New York; two at Winterthur (Montgomery, No. 74); three others are in private collections.

175 Side Chair (one of a pair)   B.69.87

New York, 1810–1820
Mahogany, ash. H.33½ W.18¼ D.19

Use of a broad crest rail extending across the stiles more nearly conforms to the ancient prototype. In this case the rail or tablet is ornamented with an inset of highly figured mahogany veneer. Placement of the legs, set back slightly from the front of the seat rail, is an unusual feature.

In the stay rail the maker has combined the favored motifs of the period, an eagle with spread wings over a pair of cornucopia, a combination that intimates the confidence of our young nation.

176 Side Chair (one of four)   B.67.27

New York, 1815–1825
Maple. H.32 W.18 D.20

Furniture with painted landscapes, both chairs and tables, found great favor in the New York area between about 1820 and 1830 (No. 191). The set of four side chairs is ornamented with differing romantic scenes incorporating ruins, mountains, and lakes or rivers. The painter has not yet been identified. He may, however, be the product of one of the several small painting academies that existed in New York in the early nineteenth century. The tablets have been made especially wide to accommodate the scenes, and the maker has adjusted his composition accordingly using a pair of smaller lyre splats. The two-part stiles with inset discs lend visual lightness without sacrifice of strength. These chairs not only represent the finest of New York landscape furniture,[5] but also belong to a group of extremely sophisticated maple pieces. Among these is a superb sofa made for John Jay.[6]

5. Related landscape examples are at Winterthur (Montgomery, No. 469); Sleepy Hollow Restorations, Tarrytown, New York (Wendel Garrett et al., *The Arts in America: The Nineteenth Century*, New York, Charles Scribner's Sons, 1969, p. 302).
6. Now in a private Texas collection.

177 Side Chair (one of a pair)   B.69.72

Philadelphia, 1815–1825
Mahogany, rosewood, ebony, ash, pine.
H.31⅝ W.18⅞ D.22¼

Based on designs by Thomas Hope, this Philadelphia chair with its wide tablet and severe rectilinear lines is more archaeological and closer to its Grecian prototype than is the norm.[7] In design the chair represents a distinct Philadelphia type; similar chairs were designed for the White House by Benjamin Latrobe,[8] and related examples were made in Baltimore.[9] The Baltimore chairs are usually painted and feature turned front legs of Roman origin. Flat planes and severity of line are relieved by lavish brass inlay as well as inlaid ebony and rosewood, in accord with the suggestions of Hope and George Smith.[10] The Philadelphia *Price Book* of 1828 reveals that brass stringing was two-and-one-half times the cost of wood, indicating that these chairs were extremely expensive.[11] Here the brass is let into the wood in the English manner rather than being applied, as was the French custom. Star shapes on the seat rail and stiles suggest the functional nail heads of antique prototypes. These chairs, part of a set of twelve, were made for the Hare family.

7. Thomas Hope, *Household Furniture & Interior Decoration, Executed from Designs by Thomas Hope*, London, 1807, Pls. 24–25.

8. *Antiques*, June 1959, p. 568.

9. William V. Elder, III, *Baltimore Painted Furniture, 1800–1840*, The Baltimore Museum of Art, 1972, Nos. 36, 49.

10. Hope, Pl. 24, No. 3.

11. *The Philadelphia Cabinet and Chair Makers' Union Book of Prices for Manufacturing Cabinet Ware*, Philadelphia, William Stavely, 1828, p. 76.

178 Side Chair (one of four)   B.67.30

Pennsylvania or New Jersey, 1815–1825
Maple, pine, painted. H.33 W.17¼ D.21

This set is part of a body of sophisticated painted furniture that found great favor in the early Empire period. The round front legs with ring turnings, adapted from Roman sources, often appear on Baltimore chairs. However, the design and painted ornament with large, stylized anthemion splat indicate a Pennsylvania or New Jersey origin.[12]

12. Chairs of virtually identical design and painted ornament, varying only in the use of a wide tablet, are at Winterthur (Montgomery, No. 466); another related pair is at Fountain Elms, Utica, New York (Comstock, No. 588).

179 Miniature Side Chair (one of a pair)   B.71.125

New York, 1830–1840
Mahogany, ash, pine. H.26¼ W.13¾ D.14¾
Gift of Mr. and Mrs. Harris Masterson

About 1830, a new chair form, based on French Restauration prototypes, became fashionable. Although the general sweeping lines of the klysmos were retained, the seat design was altered to a semicircular shape of Roman origin and the backs became curved. The front legs assumed an outward-curved console form. Plain flat surfaces were veneered with the richest dark, highly-figured mahogany. Occasionally the finest of these *chaises gondoles* were ornamented, as seen in this example, with discreet lotus leaf carving at the knees and seat rail.

180 Side Chair (one of six)   B.69.39

New Orleans, Louisiana (?), 1835–1850
Mahogany, walnut, ash. H.33⅛ W.18 D.21¾

A second variant of the *chaise gondole*, with curved as opposed to flat tablet and vase rather than straight splat, is seen here. The scrolls at either end of the tablet are the most typical motif of the Restauration style. Chairs like this and the preceding example appear as numbers 11 and 12 of the famous 1833 advertisement of Joseph Meeks and Sons. However, this particular type, often called fiddleback, found great acceptance and was made virtually in every furniture center. In New Orleans, where this set was found, they have been associated with the name of François Seignouret (working 1815–1853), and the name "Seignouret Chairs" has become a generic term for *chaises gondoles* in that area.

181 Sofa

B.68.12

Philadelphia or Baltimore, 1815–1820
Pine, poplar. H. 31 W. 29¾ L. 90

The scrolled lines of ancient classical couches have been translated into fierce symbols of the young republic. So-called Grecian or French sofas, loosely based on ancient prototypes and characterized by curving ends of unequal height, found popularity in the neoclassical period. The original design for this example appears in Sheraton's *Encyclopaedia* of 1806.[13] Even the legs, assuming the shape of cornucopia, allude to the classical past. Made of poplar and maple, the wood surfaces are entirely gilded, making an unusual piece of great sophistication.

13. Thomas Sheraton, *The Cabinet-Maker, Upholsterer and General Artist's Encyclopaedia*, London, 1804–1806, Pl. 6; illustrated, Peter Ward-Jackson, *English Furniture Designs of the Eighteenth Century*, London, H.M.S.O., 1958, Pl. 337.

182 Card Table (one of a pair)

B.69.385

New York, ca. 1810
Mahogany, pine, cherry. H. 29¾ W. 35⅜ D. 18 (closed)
36⅛ (open)

As in the earlier Chippendale period, New York Empire craftsmen evolved a very distinctive and successful form of card table. When the table is opened, the rear legs ingeniously swing back providing further stability. Vestigial remains of the earlier conventional legs are seen in the drops at the skirt. This example is distinguished by a crossbanded tablet at the center of the skirt and rich leaf carving and reeding on the legs.

183 Card Table

B.64.48

Possibly Henry Connelly, 1770–1826
Philadelphia, ca. 1810
Mahogany, pine. H. 30 W. 35 D. 17¾ (closed)
35⁹⁄₁₆ (open)

This table represents the Philadelphia expression of the early Empire style. While similar in concept to tables made in New York, several details betray its Philadelphia origin. The top is veneered with radiating rays of highly figured mahogany (No. 192).[14] The acanthus leaf carving has a loose and naturalistic quality that differs radically from the symmetrical stylized treatment of New York. The break at the top of the legs, while unusual, relates to the treatment on a group of Philadelphia lyre-base sewing tables.[15]

14. Montgomery, Nos. 316, 349.
15. Tracy, No. 20.

184 Card Table

B.68.31

New York, ca. 1824
Mahogany, pine, paint, gesso, gilt.
H. 30¾ W. 36 D. 19 (closed) 36⅝ (open)

The full Empire style card table is composed of three parts: pedestal base, intermediary supporting members and upper section. In this example, made in New York about 1824, the intermediary supporting section consists of four columns with lotus-shape capitals.[16] These may be a reference to the Egyptian taste, a leitmotif that occurs throughout the Empire style. Paint has been skillfully employed, the entire mahogany area having been grained to resemble rosewood while the eagle brackets and paw feet have been gilded and ebonized. Ormolu mounts and a brass molding further enhance the skirt.

16. It is part of a group of furniture made for Miss M. A. Babcock, one of which is inscribed and dated (Tracy, No. 47).

185 Card Table

B.68.32

New York, 1820–1830
Mahogany, rosewood, ebony, pine, brass.
H. 29½ W. 36 D. 18 (closed) 36 (open)

While the classical lyre was frequently used as a supporting member, the incorporation of griffen heads is unusual. Vigorously carved hairy paw feet with acanthus above are the New York norm. Rosewood crossbanding around the top, brass stringing and an ebony molding at the base of the skirt are small unobtrusive details which, combined with the stenciled swans at the corners and inlaid brass molding at the top of the lyre, lend subtle distinction.

186 Sofa Table

B.71.106

New York, ca. 1820
Mahogany, pine, ash, brass. H. 28½ W. 55¾ D. 27¾

Sofa tables, wrote Sheraton in his *Cabinet Dictionary* are "those used before a sofa . . . ladies chiefly occupy them to draw, write or read upon."[17] A new luxurious specialized form in the early nineteenth century, the sofa table is characteristically rectangular with small drop leaves at either end. Following Sheraton's precepts, the left-hand drawer in this example is fitted with an adjustable baize-covered writing surface and compartments for the storage of writing materials. Perhaps its most distinctive decorative feature is the handsome pair of gilt-winged caryatid figures. Derived from French Empire designs, specifically those of La Mésengère, the caryatid figure was used in a number of instances by the eminent French-born New York cabinetmaker, Charles Honoré Lannuier (1779–1819). On this table, however, the figures vary in details of carving and facial aspect. An unusual feature is the sharp step moldings that appear on the plinth at either end and above the leaf carving of the supports of the cheval base. Also uncommon is the truncated spiral cone-shape turning on the stretchers. These details, not seen elsewhere in known Lannuier examples, lend a quality

of singularity to this sofa table which suggests that another master New York craftsman was responsible.[18]

17. Thomas Sheraton, *The Cabinet Dictionary*, London, W. Smith, 1803, p. 309.

18. The mate to this sofa table is in the White House collection (Comstock, No. 589).

187   Stand   B.70.27
New York, 1815–1825
Mahogany, pine. H.27½ W.22¾ D.18½
Gift of the Friends of Bayou Bend

Although tilt-top stands were popular in the eighteenth and early nineteenth centuries, development of the form to a purely Empire expression is almost unknown. Stylistically related to card tables, the elements here have been skillfully adapted to a tripod base resulting in an unusual three-part lyre which is strung with brass rods. Brass inlay ornaments the molding of the skirt. The square top with canted corners is veneered in magnificent crotch mahogany not only on the top surface but also on the underside. It is similarly crossbanded around the edges with the result that when the top is tilted a fine finished surface is exposed on both sides.

188   Work Table   B.69.391
New York, 1810–1815
Mahogany, poplar, pine. H.29¼ W.23 D.15⅛

The small sophisticated work table represents the acme of New York furniture during the second decade of the nineteenth century in both craftsmanship and expense. A wealth of detail, such as the canted corners with recessed panels or reeded edge to the top, distinguishes this example. The top lifts to reveal a writing compartment with adjustable felt-covered work surface. Behind the tambour door are two sliding shelves with veneered mahogany fronts.[19]

19. A very similar example, varying in small details, is at Winterthur (Montgomery, No. 408).

189   Pier Table   B.69.20
Possibly Charles Honoré Lannuier, 1779–1819
New York, ca. 1815–1820
Mahogany, pine, marble. H.37⅜ W.42¼ D.18

The pier table assumed new importance as a piece of parlor furniture during the Empire period. Often made in pairs and designed to be placed between windows, the Empire pier table is usually quite architectural, incorporating columns and pilasters, as in this example. Paw feet painted verd antique are based on classical models. Leaves and lotus blossoms, motifs of Egyptian origin, ornament the gilt bronze capitals and bases, while ormolu mounts on the skirt are in the classical vein.

190 Table
B.67.40

New York, 1825–1835
Mahogany, rosewood, pine. H. 28 DIAM. 29¾

The classical tripod has been adapted to a small circular stand. Three ebonized columns with lotus capitals support the upper section while the platform stands on turned feet of Roman derivation. Freehand gilding, ornamenting the rosewood skirt and ebonized base, is combined with gilt stenciling on the columns and platform to create a brilliant visual effect.

191 Center Table
B.69.526

New York, 1825–1835
Rosewood, pine, paint. H. 26¼ DIAM. 36

Center tables, wrote Thomas Webster in his *Encyclopaedia of Domestic Economy*, "are made with the pillar extremely strong."[20] Here a plain broad columnar pedestal conforms to Webster's precepts. Simple smooth surfaces and cone-shape feet, of Roman origin, replace the elaborate carved detail and paw feet of the earlier Empire style, reflecting the Restauration taste that began to be popular about 1825. The pedestal and base are painted in imitation of rosewood. Gilt ornament appears around the skirt and on the base. However, the most remarkable feature of this table is the anonymous, skillfully painted, romantic landscape (No. 176) relating this piece to a small group of painted New York center tables.

20. Webster, p. 259.

192 Center or Loo Table
B.67.7

Philadelphia, 1825–1835
Mahogany, poplar, pine. H. 29¼ DIAM. 47⅞
Gift of Mrs. Harry C. Hanszen

The Philadelphia Cabinet and Chair Maker's Union Book of Prices for 1828 very nearly describes this example in listing "loo table with solid top three feet eight inches in diameter," and, further, that the top can be turned up "with clamps and catch." Inclusion of the form in the Philadelphia *Price Book* suggests that this sort of table was prevalent there. The design source may be plate 69 of George Smith's *Designs* where Figure 2 illustrates a closely related table with molded skirt, acanthus leaf ornament at the base of the pillar and identical squashed ball feet. Smith describes how the top turns up as usual and how the molded frame or skirt conceals the block and pin mechanism.[21] The pedestal and base are poplar, ebonized and skillfully stenciled, while the top surface is veneered in rays of richly figured mahogany. This treatment was popular in Philadelphia, appearing in the tops of slightly earlier card tables associated with Henry Connelly (No. 183).

It also appears on a group of sophisticated Philadelphia center tables ascribed to Anthony G. Quervelle.[22] The same sort of ebonized banding with gilding around the top's outer edge appears on two other Philadelphia examples. While it is not possible at this point to safely attribute this table to a Phila-

delphia maker, it can be said with certainty that it represents a distinct Philadelphia type.

21. Described, Smith, pp. 12–13.
22. *Antiques*, July 1973, p. 90.

193 Dining Table (three parts)   B.63.76

Southern, possibly Charleston, 1815–1830
Mahogany, cherry, pine.
H. 28½ W. 55 L. 69⅟₁₆ (center open) 23⅟₁₆ (each end)

At the end of the eighteenth century, with the advent of commodious rooms specifically set aside for dining, larger banquet-sized tables were introduced. Most often they consisted of a central drop-leaf section and two end sections which could be removed when the full-sized table was not required. This somewhat severe example is distinguished by turned legs of rather complicated pattern derived from the later designs of Sheraton. In fact, the turnings are similar in spirit to those of the sofa table in example No. 186. Spiral, so-called rope-leg, turning found long-continued favor in the South. According to family tradition this piece, originally owned by Captain Joseph Jones of Liberty County, Georgia, was made in Charleston.

194 Sugar Chest   B.32.69L

Kentucky, ca. 1825
Cherry, pine. H. 35½ W. 32½ D. 18½

Chests made specifically for the storage of sugar seem to be a southern American, primarily Kentucky, phenomenon. This substantial, fairly late, cherry example is ornamented on the stiles with distinctive reeding set within a sunken panel. The short, bulbous, turned legs are reeded, as is the lid edge above. The interior is divided into two deep compartments with sliding covers. The chest has a history of ownership in the Lexington area.[23]

23. The use of cherry, reeded pilasters and short feet relates this example to a group of furniture made by Robert Wilson working in Lexington, 1792–1825 (*Antiques*, May 1973, p. 946, Fig. 3).

195 Sideboard   B.61.28

Southern, probably Eastern Tennessee, 1815–1830
Cherry, mahogany, poplar, pine. H. 48½ W. 72 D. 20¼

Later sideboards became considerably heavier as further storage space was added. In this case, a recessed central section breaks the mass and adds to the visual interest created through the use of brilliant crotch-grain cherry wood framed with mahogany arches on the doors. The low china rail, a feature of Empire sideboards, is carefully conceived and, in line, echoes the recessed section below. The maker has retained short, plump, turned legs in the late Sheraton mode that lingered in the South. The original glass hardware was replaced in the twentieth century. This sideboard, found in the vicinity of Knoxville, relates to Virginia and North Carolina examples but is believed to have been made in East Tennessee.

196   Sideboard   B.67.6

Attributed to Joseph Meeks & Son, active 1797–1868
New York, 1825–1835
Mahogany, pine, paint, gilt. H.65 W.68 D.26
Gift of Mrs. Harry C. Hanszen

This massive example represents the highest expression
of the New York Empire style with elaborately designed
mahogany veneers, ebonizing and gilt ornament. In general
scheme it closely resembles number 33 of the well-known
advertisement of Joseph Meeks & Sons, although it differs in
two details, the central platform and monumental eagle feet.
The magnificent painted gilt ornament, particularly the imitation ormolu rinceau on the central drawers, is rather close to
that on a pier table bearing the Meeks label.[24] It is likely that
this sideboard also can be ascribed to the Meekses.

24. *Nineteenth Century America*, No. 28.

197 Cellarette

B.67.31

New York, 1815–1825
Mahogany, pine, paint, gilt. H. 24 W. 23 D. 23

Enthusiasm for the ancient past is reflected in the sarcophagus shape. Originally conceived *en suite* with a pedestal sideboard, this cellarette provided storage for wine and spirits.[25] The richest figured mahogany is veneered to the curved surfaces. Castors, fitted to the verd antique paw feet, provide the piece with convenient mobility, facilitating placement near the dining table when in use.

25. McClelland, Pl. 107, illustrates a similar cellarette with its sideboard.

198 Wardrobe

B.68.6

Probably Rhode Island, 1815–1825
Mahogany, poplar, pine, maple, rosewood, pewter, ebony, bone. H. 87⅛ W. 63⅛ D. 25½

The wardrobe or armoire, a continental furniture form, found new favor in America in the early years of the nineteenth century. In general design, this example with rounded corners and bold molded cornice, relates to a group made in Louisiana.[26] Ovals, inlaid with initials, also appear on the friezes of Louisiana armoires. However, the absence of fiche hinges and the unusual cypress as secondary wood indicate something other than a Louisiana origin. Satinwood panels and mariner stars as well as pewter and ivory inlays were frequently used in New England furniture. These features, plus a Rhode Island history, suggest tentatively that this wardrobe may be a high-style example of Empire cabinetmaking from Rhode Island.[27]

26. Jessie Poesch, *Early Furniture of Louisiana*, New Orleans, Louisiana State Museum, 1972, Nos. 43, 44.

27. The wardrobe bears the initials, *AG*, for Ann Gibbs who married James de Wolfe of Bristol, Rhode Island.

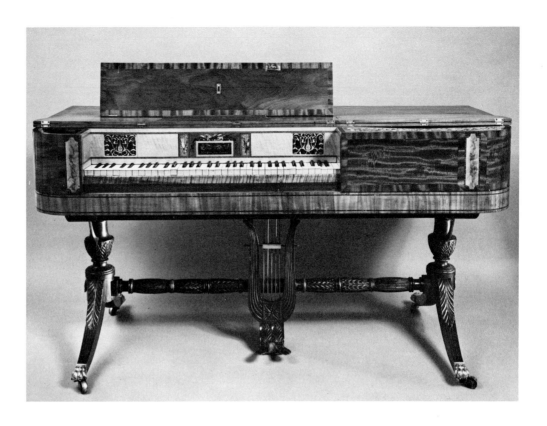

199   Pianoforte   B.57.4

Gibson and Davis, active 1801–1820
New York, ca. 1815
Mahogany, satinwood, maple, pine, brass, paint.
H. 37½   L. 71½   D. 33

About 1800, the pianoforte, an early eighteenth century
Italian invention, began to be made in appreciable numbers by
American craftsmen. Among the leading New York makers
was the firm of Thomas Gibson and Morgan Davis who were
in partnership from circa 1801 to 1820. They had been trained
in London and, taking into consideration American prejudice
for imported pianos, advertised that they were "lately arrived
in this country."[28] The sounding board of this example is skillfully painted with a pale green neoclassical panel in the center
of which is a black reserve bearing the name of *Gibson & Davis/
New York from London*, and inscribed on a ribbon above, *Patent
Grand*. This latter inscription indicates that the Bayou Bend
example is a horizontal grand piano. A number of pianofortes
with works and case by Gibson and Davis survive today.[29]

The trestle or cheval bases for these pianos, made by
leading cabinetmakers such as Duncan Phyfe, conformed to
the prevailing New York taste: sabre legs, reeding and waterleaf carving. On earlier models, pedals were absent or, when
included, were suspended from simple brass rods. Lyre supports, placed in front of the horizontal stretcher, appear to be
a later adaptation. Even later, the lyre was placed between two
smaller horizontal stretchers.

28. Rita Gottesman, *The Arts and Crafts in New York, 1800–1804*, The
New-York Historical Society, 1965, p. 331.

29. One closely related example is in the Henry Ford Museum, Dear-
born (Celia Jackson Otto, *American Furniture of the Nineteenth Century*,
New York, The Viking Press, 1965, No. 44). Another is illustrated in
McClelland, Pl. 86.

THE BELTER PARLOR.   The Belter Parlor represents a room of a fashionable household of the 1845–1870 period. Typical of the era are the high ceilings and floor-to-ceiling windows, heavy plasterwork cornices and ceiling ornament, and small, arched, coal-burning fireplace. The handsome white marble mantelpiece is magnificently carved with a profusion of floral and fruit ornament in the spandrels. Although more recently installed in the George Corliss mansion in Providence, Rhode Island, it was made originally for a house in Saratoga, New York. Parrots on swings appear on each corner, while a pair of small birds, one in the nest and one perched outside, ornament the central keystone above the arched opening.

At the windows are rich damask curtains based in design on mid-nineteenth century originals found at Lansdowne Plantation, Natchez, Mississippi. The deep central lambrequin, tassels and *passementerie* are all typical of the detail lavished on curtains at mid-century. The use of a second set of curtains, made of lace, also conforms to contemporary taste. Gilt rococo window cornices complete the opulent window treatment.

As the nineteenth century progressed wallpaper became a very important part of interior decoration. Different styles and palettes were deemed appropriate for the hall, library, dining room and parlor. Generally, parlors were papered in rococo floral patterns of light colors, often

The Rococo Revival Period 1850-1870

One of the strongest themes in American decorative arts of the nineteenth century was a revival of the rococo. The reborn rococo first flourished in France at the court of Louis Philippe (1830–1848), where the eighteenth century mode was reintroduced. By about 1840 the new taste began to appear in American furniture, and during the 1850's and early 1860's the rococo reigned supreme. It succeeded the stark simplicity of the late classical "pillar and scroll" furniture of the French Restauration style. Americans reveled in the rich fanciful ornament later described by Charles Eastlake as "a curious combination of those diverse elements of design, mixed with flowers and creeping plants meandering over the whole surface."[1]

In furniture, the cabriole legs, c- and s-scrolls and naturalistic floral ornament of the eighteenth century (Nos. 200, 209) reappeared. Although the vocabulary was the same, the interpretation of the revived rococo was completely nineteenth century. The new fashion was variously described as "French modern" or "French antique," "Louis XV" or "Louis XVI," and, although this terminology seems to suggest a certain degree of confusion amongst our mid-nineteenth century ancestors, there is no doubt that all things French, or in the French taste, were definitely à la mode.

By 1850 one of the leaders in production of rococo revival furniture was an immigrant cabinetmaker, John Henry Belter (1804–1863), who came to America from Württemberg, Germany, in 1844 and worked in New York until his death in 1863. So renowned did this craftsman's products become that even in his own era, as today, the generic term for the finest rococo revival furniture was "Belter." His reputation rests on the manufacture of the most intricately carved and perforated ornament. This was made possible through the use of laminated rosewood bent in cawls or molds under steam pressure creating remarkable curved forms. These thin, but strong, laminated surfaces could then be lavishly carved. Although Belter patented this complicated process at various times between 1847 and 1858, evidence suggests that at least two of Belter's competitors, Charles A. Boudouine (active ca. 1845–1900) and Joseph Meeks (1783–1865), infringed on his patents and manufactured very similar furniture. It is likely other leading New York cabinetmakers also worked in Belter's style.

Furniture of the rococo revival period is especially fascinating because it represents a

with matching or complementary borders. Here the paper and border have been reproduced from a mid-nineteenth century French example used at "Elmwood," built by Robert Little about 1850, in Salisbury, Connecticut. Fragments of that paper, now in the collection of the Cooper-Hewitt Museum, New York, served as documentation of the reproduction. On the floor is a wall-to-wall carpet of a type termed, generically, "Brussels." Dating from 1850 or 1860 it is probably of English manufacture and very likely the sort described by Thomas Webster as "Wilton, velvet pile lately introduced."[2] Typical of the period is the boldly colored all-over scroll and floral design, characterized by Eastlake as "large sprawling patterns."[3]

turning point in the history of furniture. The lavishly hand-carved ornament continues practices of the past while the use of bent, laminated wood anticipates later developments in furniture manufacture. Similarly, coil steel springs, first used about 1850, and the introduction of rich, occasionally tufted, upholstery (No. 202) foreshadow the overstuffed furniture and standards of greater comfort that became the rule by the end of the nineteenth century.

1. Eastlake, p. 115.
2. Webster, p. 253.
3. Eastlake, p. 112.

200 Parlor Chair (one of a pair)   B.71.33
John Henry Belter, active 1844–1863
New York, ca. 1850–1860
Rosewood, ash. H.38 W.18 D.27

Matching the sofa (No. 205), this side chair is one of two remaining from a larger set. The bold scrolled backs with flowers and oak leaves are made of a single sheet of rosewood, laminated in six layers and bent under steam pressure. The horseshoe-shape seat with serpentine front seems to be both characteristic of Belter and more common than the circular treatment of No. 202 and No. 204. A small cornucopia in the crest is echoed at the sides of the back. Rich naturalistic flowers, fruit and scrolled leafage are carved on the seat rail.

201 Parlor Chair (one of a pair)   B.57.6
New York, ca. 1850–1860
Rosewood, ash. H.38¾ W.19 D.23½

Although very similar in composition to No. 200, close examination of this chair reveals that the boldness of Belter's detail is not present. The carving is generally less three-dimensional. The seat rail lacks the sinuous serpentine outline.[4] However, the crest, carved with an asymmetrical grouping of flowers, is skillfully executed, some of the blossoms being deeply undercut. The mate to this chair has mirror asymmetry.

4. A side chair with the same seat shape, carved rail and leg, but different back, incorporating grape leaves and grapes versus oak leaves and acorns, as here, was exhibited as the work of Belter but probably represents another pattern from the same shop that produced this example (Miller, p. 83).

202 Parlor Chair (one of a pair)   B.71.36
Attributed to Alexander Roux, active 1837–1881
New York, ca. 1850–1860
Rosewood, ash. H.44 W.18 D.25

A distinctive feature of these pieces attributed to Roux (204, 206), is the ovolo molding that outlines the upholstered area of the back, separating it from the scrolled ornament. The front legs of the entire set are carved with a scale-like decoration of Renaissance design. A cartouche with flanking strapwork, vaguely reminiscent of the Renaissance revival style, appears on the center of the skirt, while rococo flowers, vines and grapes are incorporated into the laminated back. This mixture of detail is typical of the blending of modes during the late 1850's.

203 Parlor Chair

B.71.37

New York, ca. 1855–1865
Rosewood, oak, ash, pine. H. 39½ W. 17½ D. 23¼

This light and airy example is a *tour-de-force* of laminated furniture. In the center of the back, interlaced scrolls fill a void usually covered with upholstery. Turning at the top of the legs combined with strapwork on the seat rail, elements of Renaissance revival design, suggest a slightly later date than that of the preceding examples. A mate is in the Cooper-Hewitt Museum, New York.[5]

5. Comstock, No. 648.

204 Armchair (one of a pair)

B.71.35

Attributed to Alexander Roux, active 1837–1881
New York, ca. 1850–1860
Rosewood, ash, pine. H. 50 W. 22½ D. 29½

Matching No. 202 and No. 206, this armchair exhibits several features that suggest an attribution other than to Belter. In a major variation of construction, its laminated back displays a center seam or joint, a practice used by leading New York cabinetworkers to avoid infringement on Belter's patents. Moreover, the seat is round rather than the more common semicircular shape with its serpentine front. The rear legs are round in section as opposed to the rectangular shape used on No. 200 and No. 201.

205 Sofa

B.71.32

John Henry Belter, active 1844–1863
New York, ca. 1850–1860
Rosewood, ash. H. 45 W. 72 D. 34

En suite with a pair of side chairs (No. 200), this sofa was originally the smaller one of a parlor set including at least two sofas, two armchairs and six side chairs. On stylistic grounds, the three pieces at Bayou Bend have been attributed to John Belter. A tripartite composition of carved interlaced leaves and vines, bold containing scroll and crowning bouquet of flowers is closely related to the treatment on furniture made by Belter for Mrs. Samuel Milbank.[6] Recently a large parlor set made by Belter for Colonel B. S. Jordan of Georgia in 1855 has been discovered. Those pieces, which Belter described in the surviving bill as "Arabasket," match this sofa in every detail.[7]

6. *Antiques*, September 1948, p. 168.
7. This set descended in Jordan's family and was recently purchased, (along with the original bill of sale) for use in the Governor's Mansion at Austin, Texas.

206 Sofa B.71.34

Attributed to Alexander Roux, active 1837–1881
New York, ca. 1850–1860
Rosewood, ash. H. 53⅛ W. 80⅞ D. 33½

As with No. 205, this piece was originally *en suite* with a smaller sofa, a pair of armchairs now at Bayou Bend (No. 204) and six side chairs (No. 202). The rococo revival sofa characteristically has a triple-peaked curvilinear back which flows into the arms. Here, typical ornament consisting of meandering vines, flowers and grapes is carved with lacy effect through eight layers of laminated rosewood. The lightness of design, together with an absence of the bold scrolls of Belter-associated examples, suggest the hand of another master. One of the unusual features of this sofa is the pair of finely carved birds flanking a nest at the bottom of the central cartouche (No. 206, detail). A sofa with similarly placed birds was exhibited with other pieces by Alexander Roux (1837–1881) in the New York exhibition of 1853 at the Crystal Palace.[8] Two documented Roux pieces, a labeled cabinet and a set of armchairs, are decorated with closely related birds.[9] The carved leaf and rinceau detail of documented examples also resembles this work. A smaller sofa, virtually identical to this example but belonging to another parlor set, is in the St. Louis Art Museum.

8. *Antiques*, February 1968, p. 214.
9. *Antiques*, February 1968, p. 215.

207 Méridienne or Couch B.71.57

Attributed to John Henry Belter, active 1844–1863
New York, ca. 1850–1860
Rosewood, ash. H. 38⅛ W. 61¼ D. 28½

The méridienne or couch was often included in parlor furniture of the rococo revival period. This example with its bold, rich, fluid scrolls, crowned by a modest crest of flowers and fruit, relates closely to the work of Belter. Like No. 205, the back is laminated, but this piece is less ambitious. The absence of elaborate pierced design and the simplified ornament of the skirt and legs indicate this was originally a somewhat less expensive piece. It is part of a parlor set which has a history of ownership in New York by the Reverend George H. Houghton, first rector of the Church of the Transfiguration.

208 Center Table B.70.42

New York, ca. 1850–1860
Rosewood, ash. H. 30⅛ DIAM. 30⅝

Center tables remained important items of parlor furniture during the early Victorian period. This example varies from the norm in being round rather than oval. Also unusual is the fact that the marble top is set into, rather than projecting over, the frame. Typical of the rococo revival interpretation of the center table are the bold cabriole legs and the scrolled cross stretchers with central vase and finial ornament. The laminated skirt, carved with interlaced vines surrounding a central floral motif, is less three-dimensional than many examples.

209 Dressing Table

B.57.5

New Orleans, Louisiana, ca. 1850–1860
Mahogany, pine. H.68 W.45½ D.22¾

Large sets of luxurious rococo revival bedroom furniture often included an elaborate dressing table. In design this example is typical, with bold cabriole legs — here formed by paired c-scrolls — saltire stretchers, deep skirt, marble top and mirror above. While in the full-blown rococo mode, with lavish scroll and floral ornament, traces of earlier styles are retained in the fluted urn finial, the acanthus carving between the stretchers, the wavy or ripple molding at the base of the mirror section and the beading around the looking glass. An unusual feature is the horizontal rather than vertical looking glass. This dressing table has a history of ownership in Louisiana. The fluted urn finial often appears on New Orleans examples, and it is likely that the table was made there by a cabinetmaker after the mode of François Seignouret (active 1815–1853).

210 Étagère

B.71.41

Attributed to John Henry Belter, active 1844–1863
New York, ca. 1850–1860
Rosewood, poplar, pine, oak. H.97 W.51 D.16¾

The étagère or what-not, a new form, became the dominant item of case furniture in fashionable parlors during the rococo revival period. Small shelves, often backed with mirrors, were intended to provide display space for "articles of virtu — bouquets of flowers, scientific curiosities, or whatever," in short, the eclectic array of knickknacks so much a part of Victorian taste.[10] This rosewood example is similar to one made by Belter in 1855 to accompany a set of "Arabasket" furniture.[11] The semicircular commode-like section is richly overlaid with asymmetrical rococo detail, fruit on the skirt and scrolls and leafage on the three drawer fronts within the frieze. The upper section, architectural in design with pediment and colonettes, is crowned with bold floral and grape ornament. This latter motif is repeated on the laminated brackets of the semicircular shelves. Arched mirrors add extra glitter to the display of objects.

10. A. J. Downing, *The Architecture of Country Houses* (1850, facsimile reprint, New York, Dover Publications, Inc., 1969), p. 456.
11. Owned by Col. B. S. Jordan of Georgia (No. 205).

Traditional Furniture and Arts

The simple furniture and primitive art of our country have always held a special fascination for collectors of Americana. It was unsophisticated furniture, in fact, which inspired the interest of both Miss Hogg (No. 215) and Henry Francis du Pont in examples of American craftsmanship and, indeed, provided the first American acquisition for the Bayou Bend (No. 214) and Winterthur collections.[1]

In contrast to the sophisticated European products both collectors had favored previously, these unaffected objects seemed attractive, perhaps for a directness and simplicity reflective of American character, evoking the image of a less complex and more virtuous past.

It is difficult to coin a terminology for this category of American art. While it has been customarily characterized as "country" or rural, in reality many of the pieces were products of urban craftsmen working in a conservative or traditional style. Chairs made in Philadelphia by men like William Savery are a perfect example (No. 211), although the same sort of chair was also produced in rural areas. Similarly, even non-utilitarian folk objects cannot be classified as wholly rural in origin. Certainly the cigar-store Indian (No. 233) was intended for urban use; yet, other carved wooden sculpture, such as weathervanes or Schimmel's eagles, was used in the country. The fact is that this furniture and naive art are the product of common people, both urban and rural, and as such reflect the vernacular expression of their society's traditional forms. The term "traditional" has been chosen, therefore, as an inclusive description.

1. While visiting Mrs. J. Watson Webb at Shelburne, Vermont, Mr. du Pont saw a pine dresser filled with Staffordshire plates and subsequently became fascinated with American antiques. His first purchase was a 1727 Pennsylvania chest (Sweeney, p. 31).

THE MAPLE ROOM. The Maple Room represents a country bedchamber of the early nineteenth century. Suggesting several generations of continuous occupation, the paneling is based on mid-eighteenth century examples while the stenciled border, which imitates wallpaper, was derived from early nineteenth century Pittsfield, Massachusetts, work. The less sophisticated furniture, made of maple and pine, is primarily of rural origin. On the table is an English strawberry pattern creamware tea service. New England hooked rugs cover the floor.

THE TEXAS ROOM.   Cedar paneling with Gothic arches is based on a house built near the town of Liberty in East Texas during the 1850's. Southern furniture reflects the heritage of many early settlers in the eastern area of the State. In the cupboards and elsewhere are examples of *Texian Campaigne* china, made at the Mercy Pottery, Burslem, Staffordshire, to commemorate the war between the United States and Mexico (1846–1848). Lithographs of the Mexican War made by Nathaniel Currier and others hang on the walls. Above the sideboard is a portrait of Miss Hogg's grandfather, General Joseph Lewis Hogg (1806–1862), a Colonel in the Mexican War, who is portrayed here as a Brigadier General, his rank during the Civil War.

THE GLAZED PORCH. During the eighteenth century, Americans developed distinctive variants of an English stick-furniture form known as "windsor." This attractive, sturdy, yet inexpensive, seat furniture was used throughout the colonies. Examples from Pennsylvania and New England are found on a second-story glassed-in porch. The tin chandelier, one of a pair, is from a church in Connecticut.[2] A German globe, at the lower left, made during the years of the Texas Republic (1836–1845), shows Texas as an independent nation.

2. A larger chandelier of identical design is at Winterthur (Sweeney, p. 145).

THE STAFFORDSHIRE HALL.   After the emergence of the United States as a nation,
English potters began to manufacture goods designed specifically for the American trade. Here,
blue and white transfer-printed earthenware made in Staffordshire by William Adams, Ralph
and James Clews and others, depicts such scenes as Bulfinch's Boston State House, the 1824
landing of Lafayette, Niagara Falls, the Baltimore and Ohio Railroad and views of American
cities. On the floor are utilitarian stoneware crocks, made in Rochester, New York, and Ben-
nington, Vermont.

THE WINEDALE COTTAGE. Texas-German architecture of rural Fayette and Washington counties was the basis for the Winedale Cottage interior.[3] Using colors typical of that area, the plank walls are painted pale green, the dado panels salmon pink and the trim, dark brown. On the far wall is a portrait of Lewellyn, Warwick, Walter and Ella Jones painted in Galveston by Thomas Flintoff (ca. 1809–1892) in 1851.[4] At the right, above the Texas slant-front desk, is "The Texian Hare," by John Woodhouse Audubon (1812–1862).[5]

3. The room, used as a guest reception area, derives its name from Fayette County's Winedale Inn, which was restored by Miss Hogg during the 1960's (*Antiques*, July 1968, pp. 96–100).
4. Pinckney, pp. 57–68.
5. *Viviparous Quadrupeds of North America*, 5 Vols. (1842–1854), "Lepus Texianus," PL. CXXXIII.

211 Armchair

B.66.24

Philadelphia, 1730–1800
Maple. H.46 W.26 D.18

The seventeenth century slat-back chair form, which survived into the eighteenth century, found great popularity in the Delaware Valley.[6] There, on the finest examples, the slats were arched and numbered at least five. The arms of this example are cut in the typical Pennsylvania manner, and the seat has been carefully framed in figured maple.

6. Nancy Goyne Evans, "Unsophisticated Furniture in Philadelphia," *Country Cabinetwork and Simple City Furniture*, The Henry Francis du Pont Winterthur Museum, 1970, pp. 165–167. Similar examples are illustrated (Hornor, Pl. 164; Nutting, No. 1903; Kirk, *American Furniture*, Nos. 23, 24).

212 Side Chair (one of a pair)

B.58.148.1

Delaware Valley, 1730–1800
Maple. H.45¼ W.18¼ D.22

Although slat-back side chairs of this type have been associated with the New Jersey chairmaker, Maskell Ware[7] (1776–1855), the form was in fact made in quantity throughout the lower Delaware Valley.[8] The seat is attractively finished with a scalloped skirt.

7. Margaret White, *Early Furniture Made in New Jersey*, Newark, The Newark Museum, 1958, pp. 18–20.
8. Nutting, Nos. 1897, 1907; Schiffer, Pl. 116; Randall, No. 142.

213 Armchair

B.69.223

Philadelphia, 1740–1765
Maple. H.42½ W.24¾ D.17½

During much of the eighteenth century, rush-bottom chairs found great favor in Philadelphia among all classes. This example, with a Queen Anne back and cabriole legs — called "crookt feet" — is one of the more stylish varieties. Although it is very similar to chairs associated with William Savery (1721–1788),[9] there are several differences: the usual unornamented double side stretchers (No. 211) have been supplanted with a single finely turned member which swells gently in the center, and the front stretcher follows conventional William and Mary form.

9. Hornor, Pl. 462; Downs, No. 26; *Antiques*, December 1967, p. 838.

214 Armchair   B.20.I

New England, probably Connecticut, 1735–1790
Maple. H.45⅝ W.24⅛ D.20½

This chair, transitional from the William and Mary to the Queen Anne style, is of a type made throughout New England (No. 215). Extremely slender splats, however, are often found in Connecticut work.[10] A related side chair appears in a needlework picture of Connecticut origin, and a similar example is in the Henry Ford Museum, Dearborn.[11] The bold stylized Portuguese feet are unique.

10. Kirk, *Connecticut Furniture*, No. 226; Nutting, Nos. 2100–2101.
11. Bishop, Nos. 78–79.

215 Armchair   B.68.3

New England, 1735–1790
Maple. H.45½ W.22⅞ D.22½

Although similar to the preceding example, this chair incorporates a more fully developed Queen Anne-style back and single, spindle-shaped side stretchers, a later stylistic feature.

216 Side Chair (one of a pair)   B.69.510.I

New York, 1760–1815
Maple. H.41 W.19⅜ D.14⅜

Although chairs of this design have been called "Hudson Valley," they were made also in Northern New Jersey, Long Island and Connecticut.[12] The turned form of earlier styles has been updated by the introduction of a yoke crest, splat, trumpet leg and pad foot. While the stylistic origin of these chairs is not clear, similar trumpet-shaped legs with pad feet appear on rural English furniture.[13] The form continued to be made into the early nineteenth century.[14]

12. *Antiques*, October 1936, pp. 168–170.
13. Kirk, *Connecticut Furniture*, No. 275.
14. Rice, p. 38. A number of similar examples are illustrated (Comstock, Nos. 163–164; Downs, No. 99; Bishop, No. 96; Charles Hummel, *With Hammer in Hand*, Charlottesville, The University of Virginia Press, 1968, Nos. 190C, 190D, 190E).

217   Side Chair   B.69.224

Possibly Connecticut, 1760–1815
Maple. H.40½ W.20 D.14

While similar to the preceding example, this chair differs
in several details. The splat, which is more elaborate in outline,
is reminiscent of those on Connecticut chairs, and the absence
of a ring in the medial stretcher is a feature common to other
turned chairs of Connecticut origin.[15]

15. *Antiques*, October 1936, p. 169, Fig. 7; Kirk, *Connecticut Furniture*,
Nos. 219, 220, 224.

218   Corner Chair   B.69.41

New England, 1770–1800
Maple, painted. H.29½ W.26 D.24⅛

Although turned members and a Portuguese foot might
suggest an early date, the curved seat and pierced splat indicate
that this chair was made considerably later in the eighteenth
century. It is similar to two other New England examples.[16]

16. Comstock, No. 45; Bishop, No. 116.

219   Armchair   B.69.413

Philadelphia, 1750–1780
Maple, pine, ash, hickory. H.44¾ W.26¼ D.20

An early high-back windsor armchair, this example reflects some of the unmistakable traits of the Pennsylvania style:
the attenuated vase arm supports, u-shaped saddle seat and
cylindrical lower sections of the legs. Often thought of as
"country furniture," windsor chairs were actually first introduced and made in the cities. Windsor furniture was rarely left
in its natural wood finish, and minute traces of red paint attest
to what may have been this chair's original color.

220 Side Chair (one of four)

B.71.130.2

Pennsylvania, 1840–1860
Pine, painted. H.33¼ W.18⅜ D.20½

The so-called balloon-back chair was a rural Pennsylvania adaptation of the Restauration style *chaise gondole*. It was commonly painted dark brown or green and stenciled in bronze powder shaded with bright transparent colors.[17]

17. Lea, pp. 137–147.

221 Bench

B.71.131

Pennsylvania, 1840–1860
Pine, painted. H.33½ L.69⅜ D.21⅝

Painted seat furniture was popular with the Pennsylvania Germans during the first half of the nineteenth century. Often both benches and chairs were decorated with stenciled ornament, primarily fruit or flowers. While similar to that of New England, Pennsylvania stenciling was not so intricate and was shaded with transparent color washes. Typical of Pennsylvania chair design are the wide tablet with ogee corners, stay rail and short spindles.[18]

18. Lea, pp. 148–150.

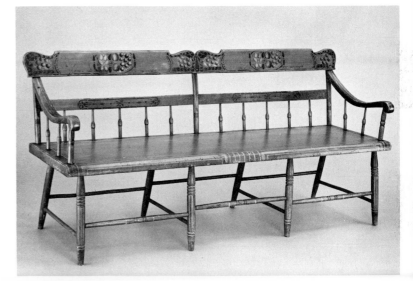

222 Tea Table

B.69.212

North Carolina, 1780–1810
Maple, pine. H.28 W.27¼ D.16½

At the end of the eighteenth century the Chippendale style lingered in rural areas, especially in the inland South. This simple tea table in the Chinese taste was found in North Carolina and probably was made there. Worm damage indicates that the surface was originally painted.

223 Stand

B.62.50

Washington County, Texas, 1850–1870
Pine. H.30 W.26 D.23¾

After 1848 a large number of German settlers came to Texas. Among them were many cabinetmakers who brought with them the late classical, early Victorian, Biedermeier style. Tables made by these men often had tapering legs, flaring at the bottom in conformance with German prototypes. This pine example has been stained dark brown in imitation of walnut.

According to the late classical German taste for simple uncluttered lines, the drawer was originally knobless. A semi-circular notch on the drawer bottom provided a finger hold. Mortise and tenon construction has been used throughout.

224 Draw Table

B.69.444

Fayette County, Texas, 1850–1870
Walnut, oak.
H.29½ D.35⅞ L.38¾ (closed) 71½ (open)

The draw table, a seventeenth century space-saving form which survived in Germany, was introduced in Texas by the German settlers. This example, with its simple lines and rounded corners, is in the classical Restauration style.

225 High Chest

B.69.231

New Hampshire, 1760–1790
Maple, pine. H.89¼ W.40⅜ D.19⅛

Furniture made in rural areas often used design motifs in unorthodox ways. This high chest is one of the most successful examples of country cabinetwork. While the continuous pediment with heart-shaped piercing has no known parallel, other features are reminiscent of New Hampshire work. Repetition of fans and wheels is not unlike the multiple ornament found on pieces associated with the Dunlops; and the almost kneeless cabriole legs are quite similar to those of identified New Hampshire pieces.[19] The single large drawer of the lower section has been paneled to give the appearance of six small drawers, a treatment which occurs on other New Hampshire chests.[20]

19. Randall, *New Hampshire*, Nos. 18, 46; Charles Parsons, "The Dunlops of New Hampshire and Their Furniture," *Country Cabinetwork and Simple City Furniture*, The Henry Francis du Pont Winterthur Museum, 1970, pp. 117, 128.

20. Parsons, pp. 128–129.

226 Desk

B.62.48

Washington County, Texas, 1860–1890
Walnut, Cedar. H. 52¾ W. 39½ D. 42

The finest examples of Texas-German furniture were made of walnut and used both mortise and tenon and dovetail construction. Typical of the Texas-German style are the fanciful gallery and scrollwork around the interior opening. The heavy rope-like inlay, however, is unusual. Another desk with a virtually identical interior has a history of being made by Otto Noak (working in the 1880's).

227 Wall Cupboard

B.71.22

Southern Virginia or Piedmont, North Carolina, 1800–1820
Walnut, pine. H. 95½ W. 49¼ D. 20½

Exuberant neoclassical ornament applied to a conservative Chippendale style form suggests a rural origin for this tall cupboard. Country cabinetmakers continued to produce such walnut furniture in central Pennsylvania, the Valley of Virginia and the North Carolina Piedmont area during the early years of the nineteenth century.[21] Here, the classical urn with trailing vines relates to inlaid ornament used in the Virginia and Piedmont regions.[22] Below the vine, reeded herringbone ornament is similar to motifs used by the Swisegood School of Davidson County, North Carolina, with the stylized reeded leaves related in spirit.[23] A sharp return at the top of the dovetailed bracket foot is a distinctive feature but, to date, is not identified according to provenance.

21. Frank L. Horton and Carolyn T. Weekley, *The Swisegood School of Cabinet Making*, Winston-Salem, Old Salem Inc., 1973, No. 13.

22. *Antiques*, January 1952, p. 88, Fig. 122; *Antiques*, January 1967, p. 115, Fig. 27; Comstock, No. 521; Horton and Weekley, No. 5.

23. Horton and Weekley, Nos. 5, 6, 15.

228 Tall Clock   B.69.230

Pennsylvania, Mahantango Valley?, 1815–1825
Pine. H. 100 W. 20⅛ D. 11¼

Although examples of painted Pennsylvania German
furniture are relatively common, grained and painted tall clocks
are rare. The distelfink, a favored Pennsylvania German motif,
ornaments the door. The turned legs and painted inlays, stringing and fans are reminiscent of details appearing on desks and
chests from the Mahantango Valley,[24] while the arched branches
at the top of the hood recall the decoration of an earlier Mahantango painted clock in the Philadelphia Museum.[25]

24. *Antiques*, May 1973, pp. 932–939.
25. *Pennsylvania Dutch Folk Arts, Philadelphia Museum of Art from the
Geesey Collection and others*, The Philadelphia Museum of Art, 1959, p. 14

Traditional Arts

229 Rooster Weathervane   B.55.10

New England, ca. 1850–1875
Iron. H. 33 W. 36

The weathervane reached an apex of popularity on the
farms of nineteenth century America. Perhaps the most prevalent form was the rooster. This large stylized example successfully captures the essence and character of that proud king of
the barnyard. The body is cast iron while the tail is made of
sheet iron. Several other virtually identical examples are known,
indicating that this weathervane was produced in a factory
rather than being home-made.[26]

26. *Plain and Fancy: A Survey of American Folk Art*, New York, Hirschl
and Adler Galleries, 1970, Fig. 90; *The Edith Halpert Folk Art Collection
Property of Terry Dintenfoss*, New York, Sotheby Parke Bernet Inc.,
November 14, 15, 1973, No. 27.

230 Sheep   B.71.88

New England, probably Massachusetts, nineteenth
century
Unidentified wood, painted. H. 32¼ L. 38⅜ W. 14

During the nineteenth century, carved wooden figures
often served as visual indicators of the product sold or manufactured. The most famous of these were the cigar-store Indians
(No. 233). This naturalistic sheep originally stood outside a
woolen mill in Lowell, Massachusetts.

231 Eagle
B.55.6

American, nineteenth century
Unidentified wood, painted. H. 37 W. 60

The ferocity of this eagle is a typical nineteenth century interpretation of our national emblem. Although the original use is not clear, it may have served as an architectural ornament, intended to be seen from below as indicated by the plain, uncarved upper sides of the wings. The same treatment appears on a related smaller eagle made for a Hudson River towboat.[27] Although the Bayou Bend example has been painted in natural colors for many years, traces of gold indicate that in its original state this great bird was gilded.

27. Welsh, Fig. 11.

232 Eagle
B.57.69

Wilhelm Schimmel, 1817–1890
Cumberland County, Pennsylvania, 1875–1890
Pine, painted. H. 11⅝ W. 17 D. 8¾

Shortly after the Civil War, Wilhelm Schimmel, a German immigrant, came to live in Cumberland County. There, using scrap lumber, he whittled various animal figures which he traded for meals and drink. Perhaps the most famous product of this itinerant folk sculptor are his spread-wing eagles. Crisp, sure strokes give these creatures a spontaneous, yet stylized, faceted surface, creating birds that are very Germanic in appearance. These eagles were made in varying sizes; the larger ones were intended for use outside, while the smaller were covered with gesso and painted. This medium-sized version is dark green.[28]

28. Similar examples are at the Smithsonian Institution, Washington, D.C., and at Shelburne Museum, Vermont (Welsh, Fig. 51; Winchester, p. 297); a large collection of Schimmel eagles is at Winterthur, and other examples are at the Metropolitan Museum, New York, and the Philadelphia Museum. Schimmel's work has been thoroughly discussed by Milton E. Flavin (*Antiques*, October 1943, pp. 164–166; *Antiques*, June 1960, pp. 586–587; *William Schimmel and Aaron Mountz: Wood Carvers*, Williamsburg, The Abby Aldrich Rockefeller Museum, 1965).

233 Tobacconist Figure
B.68.17

American, 1840–1860
Unidentified wood, painted. H. 72

Although tobacconist figures appeared in America as early as the eighteenth century, they did not reach their greatest popularity until after 1850. The majority of these figures, intended to stand in front of shops as trade signs, held tobacco products: leaves, cigars or a box of snuff. This example wears a string of tobacco leaves over her shoulder. While she is readily recognizable as an Indian, her delicate facial features reflect the neoclassical taste of the early nineteenth century. This aspect in combination with the fine quality of the carving suggests she was made about mid-century.

Paintings

234 *Boy in Brown* B.62.39

Attributed to the Pierpont Limner, active ca. 1711–1716
Probably Boston, ca. 1715
Oil on canvas. H.29½ W.24½

This painting is one of approximately ten portraits by an unknown artist working at the end of the first decade of the eighteenth century.[1] Among them are likenesses of the *Reverend* and *Mrs. James Pierpont*, dated 1711, which family tradition relates were painted in Boston by an immigrant English artist.[2] Several of the other subjects either lived in Boston or had Boston connections, suggesting that this man, known as the Pierpont Limner, was painting there. His work, which reflects the style of Sir Godfrey Kneller (1646–1723), usually depicts a bust-length figure within an oval. The composition, dramatic lighting and casual attire of *Boy in Brown* recall Kneller's *Self-Portrait* of 1685.[3]

The Pierpont Limner's portraits of *Elisha* and *Richard Lord* employ a composition and technique similar to the Bayou Bend picture, but the portrait of *Edward Collins* is virtually identical. Indeed, its subject bears sufficient resemblance to that of *Boy in Brown* to be a relative.[4]

1. William Lamson Warren, "The Pierpont Limner and Some of his Contemporaries," *The Connecticut Historical Society Bulletin*, Hartford, Connecticut Historical Society, October 1958.
2. At the Yale University Art Gallery (Warren, "Pierpont Limner," pp. 114–115).
3. In the National Portrait Gallery, London (J. Douglas Stewart, *Sir Godfrey Kneller*, London, The National Portrait Gallery, 1971, p. 14).
4. Warren, "Pierpont Limner," p. 122; *Hudson Valley Paintings 1700–1750 in the Albany Institute of History and Art*, Albany, The Albany Institute, 1959, p. 21.

235 *Ebenezer Coffin*, 1678–1730 B.63.75

Anonymous
Probably Boston, ca. 1725–1730
Oil on canvas. H.44¼ W.34¼

Ebenezer, the son of James and Mary Severance Coffin, and his wife, Eleanor Barnard (1679–1769), were born on the island of Nantucket. This portrait descended in their family.

The naive rendering of grand pose and baroque composition recalls mezzotint-inspired New York works by the Patroon painters.[5] Inclusion of Coffin's whaler, the *Nonsuch*, conforms to the tradition of incorporating details of the sitter's occupation. The probability of a print source for this picture is suggested by a portrait of *Richard Ward* (1689–1763) with identical composition.[6] Another portrait, now at the Shelburne Museum, Vermont, uses a mirror image composition. The question is complicated, however, by the existence of another somewhat more sophisticated oil on wood portrait of *Ebenezer Coffin* which is identical, except for its size (13¼ × 10). It is signed *R. Feake* (sic) and dated *1728*.[7]

The Bayou Bend portrait appears to have been copied from the small oil on wood. Assuming that the signature is authentic, the identity of R. Feake and his connection with the Coffins is a subject for further study.

5. Belknap, Pl. LI.
6. Collection of the Preservation Society of Newport County (Richard

J. Boyle, *American Paintings from Newport from the Redwood Library and Other Collections*, The Wichita Art Museum, 1970, No. 2).

7. *American Provincial Paintings 1680–1860*, Pittsburgh, Department of Fine Arts, Carnegie Institute, 1941, No. 8.

236   *Samuel Pemberton, 1723–1779*   B.72.7
      John Smibert, 1688–1751
      Boston, 1734
      Oil on canvas. H. 30¼ W. 24¼

Samuel Pemberton was the youngest son of James and Hannah Penhollow Pemberton of Boston. His portrait, which was painted in the same year as those of his sisters Mary (No. 237) and Hannah, is recorded in Smibert's *Notebook* in an entry dated May 1734: *Mr. J. Pembertons Yr. Son/Hp 3/4 25-0-0*.[8] A fourth family member, James Pemberton, Jr. (1713–1756), was painted by Smibert in 1737.[9]

Neither Samuel nor Mary Pemberton married. Accordingly, their portraits became the possessions of Hannah, who married Benjamin Colman in 1739, and they descended in the Colman family. Each picture retains its original frame.

The painting of Samuel, pictured in a grey coat and waistcoat, is a sensitive rendering of an eleven year old on the verge of adolescence. Smibert's composition, a half-length figure in a painted oval, is in the tradition of English baroque portraiture established by Sir Peter Lely (1618–1680) and Sir Godfrey Kneller. The size, 30 × 25, had become standard for bust-length portraits by the early eighteenth century. Since it equalled three-fourths of a yard, this small canvas was often called three-quarters, a terminology used in Smibert's *Notebook* entry.

8. *Notebook*, p. 92, Nos. 94, 98, 99; Hannah Pemberton's portrait is at the Metropolitan Museum, New York (Gardner and Feld, pp. 4–5).

9. *Notebook*, p. 94, No. 131.

REFERENCES. Bayley, p. 413; Foote, pp. 178–179; *Notebook*, pp. 92, 110.
EXHIBITIONS. Boston, Museum of Fine Arts, 1878; Boston, Museum of Fine Arts, *One Hundred Colonial Portraits*, 1920, p. 68; New Haven, Connecticut, Yale University Art Gallery, *The Smibert Tradition*, 1949, No. 23.

237   *Mary Pemberton, 1717–1763*   B.72.8
      John Smibert, 1688–1751
      Boston, 1734
      Oil on canvas. H. 30¼ W. 24¼

Mary Pemberton was the sister of Samuel Pemberton (No. 236). Smibert's *Notebook* records her portrait and that of her sister Hannah in July 1734.[10] All three Pemberton pictures are identical in size and format and were perhaps conceived to hang together. Mary's head tilts to her right while Hannah's is turned in the opposite direction. She wears a greenish-blue gown with a pink ribbon at the bodice.

10. *Notebook*, p. 92, Nos. 99, 98. Each is listed as a three-quarter portrait, cost £25.

REFERENCES. Bayley, p. 411; *Notebook*, pp. 92, 111.
EXHIBITIONS. Boston, Museum of Fine Arts, 1878; Boston, Museum of Fine Arts, *One Hundred Colonial Portraits*, 1920, p. 68; New Haven, Connecticut, Yale University Art Gallery, *The Smibert Tradition*, 1949, No. 22.

238 *Mrs. William Lambert*   B.59.97
John Smibert, 1688–1751
Boston, 1735
Oil on canvas. H. 35⅕ W. 27½

William Lambert (1681–1749) of Boston and his wife, Hannah, were painted by Smibert in 1734 and 1735.[11] Mr. Lambert's will in 1749 bequeathed both pictures to his nephew in whose family they descended.[12] The portrait of *Hannah Lambert*, larger and more ambitious than those of the Pemberton children (Nos. 236, 237), incorporates contraposto pose and elegant mannered hand in the best English baroque style. This painting and that of *Mr. Lambert* are the intermediate size evolved by Kneller for his portraits for the Kit-Kat Club where the slightly larger canvas permitted inclusion of at least one hand. Smibert's *Notebook* entry uses the term *K K* (Kit-Kat) in describing this picture.[13] The painting has its original frame.

11. *Notebook*, Nos. 89, 110.
12. Foote, p. 166.
13. *Notebook*, Nos. 89, 110.

EXHIBITIONS. New Haven, Connecticut, Yale University Art Gallery, *The Smibert Tradition*, 1949, No. 17.

239 *Anne McCall*, b. 1720 *(opposite)*   B.71.81
Robert Feke, 1707–1752
Philadelphia, 1746
Oil on canvas. H. 49 W. 39

Anne McCall was the second daughter of George and Anne Yeates McCall of Philadelphia. During Robert Feke's 1746 visit to Philadelphia, he painted portraits of Anne, her sister Mary and their mother, Mrs. George McCall. A younger sister Margaret was painted by the artist on his return to Philadelphia in 1749.[14] The portraits of Anne and Margaret McCall, which descended in the family of their niece Anne McCall Willing, lost their identity in the nineteenth century and only recently have been correctly re-identified.[15]

Anne McCall's picture is closely related to other works painted in Philadelphia by Feke, and the pose is nearly identical to that of *Mrs. Charles Willing* in a portrait now at Winterthur.[16] A mezzotint of *Queen Caroline* by John Faber (1684–1756), after the Queen's portrait by Joseph Highmore (1692–1780), was the basis for both pictures. Mrs. Willing's portrait, signed and dated 1746, is important in confirming the date and authorship of the painting of *Anne McCall*, which is neither signed nor dated. Although Feke copied the Highmore pose and background, he changed the position of the arms, reduced the scale of architecture and domesticated the surroundings by removing the crown and sceptre. The work is painted in the grand baroque style incorporating iconographical elements — column, marble table and drapery — which were intended to convey the feeling of authority and stature. Anne McCall wears a blue dress with a pink central panel in the skirt, indicating that this portrait may have been conceived as an ensemble with those of Mrs. McCall and Mary. All three wear the same dress and the single

flowers held by the daughters echo those in each hand of the mother.

14. R. Peter Mooz, "Anne McCall by Robert Feke," *The Bulletin*, The Museum of Fine Arts, Houston, December 1971, pp. 151–154.

15. *Antiques*, November 1968, pp. 702–707.

16. Mooz, "Anne McCall," Fig. 3.

REFERENCES. Henry Wilder Foote, *Robert Feke*, Cambridge, Harvard University Press, 1930, pp. 205–206; R. Peter Mooz, "New Clues to the Art of Robert Feke," *Antiques*, November 1968, p. 702.

EXHIBITIONS. Philadelphia, Pennsylvania Academy of Fine Arts, 1887–1888; Philadelphia, The Museum of Art, 1967–1971; Philadelphia, Academy of Fine Arts, *Philadelphia Painting and Printing to 1776*, 1971, p. 9.

240   *John Gerry*, 1741–1786   B.53.13
       Joseph Badger, 1708–1765
       Boston, ca. 1745
       Oil on canvas. H. 50 W. 36

John Gerry was the son of Thomas and Elizabeth Greenleaf Gerry of Boston and a brother of Elbridge Gerry (1744–1814). At the lower left of the canvas, the portrait bears an inscription indicating that he was three years, eight months old when painted. As Gerry was born on October 8, 1741, Badger thus would have executed the picture in June 1745. The portrait descended from John Gerry to his daughter Sarah Gerry Orne, in whose family it remained until acquired for Bayou Bend in 1953.

Badger frequently borrowed his composition from mezzotints after English portraits, as would seem to be the origin of the features here — the grand pose, monumental architecture and ideal landscape in the background. Although an early example of Badger's work, in composition the painting relates to his later portrait of *Captain Joseph Larabee* (1760).[17] There are also certain similarities to the 1760 portrait of the artist's grandson, *James Badger* (1757–1817), who was approximately the same age when painted.[18] Gerry wears a red coat and breeches; his waistcoat is pale blue.[19]

17. At the Worcester (Massachusetts) Art Museum.

18. Gardner and Feld, pp. 15–16.

19. The portrait came to Bayou Bend along with a red moreen coat that descended in the family and is thought to be the one portrayed here.

241   *Priscilla Brown Greenleaf*   B.59.98
       John Greenwood, 1727–1792
       Boston, ca. 1748
       Oil on canvas. H. 33¼ W. 27¼

The subject of this picture has been identified as Priscilla Brown whose husband, Judge Robert Brown (1682–1775), was painted by Greenwood in 1748.[20] However, the fact that Mrs. Brown died in 1744 clearly indicates a different sitter.[21] Whereas Judge Brown's portrait descended in the Greenleaf family of Boston, this painting remained in the Brown family of Plymouth. In 1743 a Priscilla Brown of Plymouth (undoubtedly a daughter of Robert) married John Greenleaf of Boston.[22] It seems reasonable to assume that the subject of the painting here is Priscilla Brown, the daughter, painted at about the same time as her father's portrait and hung in her father's house in Plymouth.

The composition, which was probably derived from a mezzotint source, shows the influence of Feke's Boston work of the late 1740's, particularly in the arrangement of the hands and lace ruffles at the sleeves. The identical pose and composition appear in another portrait attributed to Badger.[23]

20. Alan Burroughs, *John Greenwood in America 1745–1753*, Andover, Massachusetts, Phillips Academy, 1943, p. 16. A copy of that portrait is in the Bayou Bend Collection (B.55.16).

21. It is very similar to the portrait of Lois Pickering Orne painted in 1749 (Burroughs, p. 24).

22. *Plymouth County Marriages 1692–1746*, 1900. Her sister, Mary (1728–1797), was married to William Greenleaf (1725–1803). Their portraits were painted by Blackburn.

23. *Elizabeth Franklin*, at the Brooklyn Museum (Burroughs, p. 37).

242   *Margaret Nicholls*, b. 1699   B.69.344
      John Wollaston, active 1749–1769
      New York, 1749
      Oil on canvas. H. 30 W. 25
      Gift of Mr. and Mrs. Harris Masterson in memory
      of Libbie Johnston Masterson

Wollaston's portrait of *Mrs. Margaret Nicholls* was painted in the year of his arrival in America. A contemporary inscription on the reverse side gives the age of the subject as fifty years and the date, 1749. A second inscription in another hand reads *Mrs. Margt Nicholls of New York N. America/Grand Mother to Mrs. Frances Montresor*.[24]

The waist-length figure placed within a painted oval is typical of the greatest number of Wollaston's New York portraits. Stylistically, the lighter, intimate quality and nervous line of the lace passages reflect English rococo developments mastered by Wollaston during the 1740's. It has been suggested that Wollaston had studied under a London drapery painter, and indeed the rich champagne-colored silk of Mrs. Nicholl's dress reveals Wollaston's special ability to render fabrics.[25]

24. Frances Montresor, third wife of James Gabriel Montresor, was the stepmother of Colonel John Montresor whose portrait by Copley is in the Detroit Institute of Arts (Prown, I, Fig. 295).

25. Wayne Craven, "Painting in New York City," *American Painting to 1776 a Reappraisal*, The Henry Francis du Pont Winterthur Museum, 1971, p. 258.

243   *Catherine Walton Thompson*, 1729–1807   B.54.23
      John Wollaston, active 1749–1769
      New York, ca. 1750
      Oil on canvas. H. 30 W. 25

Catherine Walton was the daughter of Jacob and Marian Beekman Walton of New York. She married James Thompson, an Irish gentleman, who was a business partner of her brothers, Jacob and William Walton. Her modest bust-length portrait was painted within a year or two of her sister-in-law *Cornelia Beekman Walton* (1708–1786).[26] Both subjects wear blue, square-necked dresses of the same design.

Wollaston's composition here is similar to that used for the portrait of *Mrs. Nicholls* (No. 242), with the omission of the

painted oval. The subject has the low brow and almond-shaped eyes that are present in virtually all of his works. While this feature had long been thought to be peculiar to Wollaston, it is now recognized to be an elegant mannerism seen in certain English portraiture of the 1740's.

26. At the New York Historical Society (Belknap, Pl. XXII).

244 *Augustus Keppel*, 1725–1786   B.69.343
John Wollaston, active 1749–1769
Virginia, ca. 1755
Oil on canvas. H. 50 W. 40
Gift of Mr. and Mrs. Harris Masterson in memory
of Libbie Johnston Masterson

Augustus, Viscount Keppel (1725–1786), enjoyed a long and distinguished naval career: In 1744 he circumnavigated the globe with Anson; four years later he defeated the piratical Dey of Algiers; and at the end of his service he was Admiral in Command of the English Fleet.[27]

In late 1754, Keppel departed England to take command of the ships of the North American Station. By February 1755, Keppel, in his flagship *Norwich* along with two other vessels, had anchored off Hampton Roads.[28] At that time he apparently visited Williamsburg where this portrait was painted by Wollaston, who was then working in Virginia.

In the picture Wollaston incorporated several iconographical details — the long glass, cannon and ship at anchor — that appear to have been customary for portraits of naval personages.[29] Stylistically, it shares characteristics with his New York portrait of *Staats Long Morris* and the Maryland portrait of *Charles Carroll of Duddington*; it stands among the finest of Wollaston's Virginia works.[30] Keppel wears a blue coat and white waistcoat, both of which are trimmed with silver braid.

27. Admiral Keppel's portrait was also painted by George Romney (*Antiques*, November 1970, p. 696).

28. Clifford Dowdey, *The Golden Age*, Boston, Little Brown and Company, 1970, p. 127.

29. Thomas Gainsborough's *Admiral Augustus John, Earl of Bristol;* Ralph Earl's *Admiral Richard Kempenfelt.*

30. *American Masters 18th and 19th Centuries*, New York, Kennedy Galleries, 1973, Nos. 1, 2.

245 *William Holmes*, b. 1762   B.54.20
John Wollaston, active 1749–1769
Charleston, South Carolina, ca. 1767–1769
Oil on canvas. H. 29⅞ W. 32

William Holmes, the son of Isaac and Rebecca Bee Holmes of Charleston,[31] was painted by Wollaston, who had, in 1767, returned to America after a nine-year absence and was working in that city.[32] In the interval between his mid-1750's work and his Charleston painting, Wollaston's style had become more fully rococo as exemplified here by the informality of pose — the subject pausing momentarily from play with his pet dog. He wears a pale, shimmering brown coat and a pink waistcoat. The soft light behind the sitter's head is a feature seen only in Wollaston's Charleston work.[33] About two years earlier, John Singleton Copley (1738–1815) had painted a portrait of William's brother, John Bee Holmes.[34] John's portrait, which is virtually the same size, also includes a pet, in this case a squirrel on a chain. William faces the opposite direction from John, suggesting that Wollaston may have conceived this picture as a pendant to the Copley portrait.

31. Isaac Holmes was a Bostonian and related to the Coffins and Amorys. Copley painted portraits of several members of this family (Prown, I, p. 148).

32. This portrait is undoubtedly the one attributed to Copley and later to Jeremiah Theus (Middleton, p. 138).

33. Letter from Miss Carolyn Weekley, September 1971.

34. Prown, I, Fig. 160.

246 *Mrs. Isaac Winslow and Hannah?* B.54.32
Attributed to Joseph Blackburn, active 1754–1762
Boston, ca. 1760
Oil on canvas. H. 37 W. 28¾

The seated mother with squirming infant recalls Blackburn's 1755 painting *Isaac Winslow with his Family*.[35] Although the characterization of both the mother and child is considerably more penetrating than that of the Winslow group, there are a number of features that suggest an attribution to Blackburn. The position of the mother, seated at a right angle to the picture plane, was used by Blackburn in several other portraits of the late 1750's and early 1760's.[36] Dimly visible to the left is an opening which reveals an ideal landscape, a treatment rather similar to his 1758 portrait of *Mrs. Jonathan Simpson*.[37] Beads at the bodice, the sleeve and in the hair were often worn by Blackburn subjects. In this portrait Blackburn uses a more realistic and less decorative style, perhaps in response to the growing realism of Copley during the late 1750's.

35. *American Paintings*, I, p. 32.

36. Katherine B. Susman, *The Painting Collection of the New Haven Colony Historical Society*, The New Haven Colony Historical Society, 1971, p. 71; *The Painter and the New World*, Montreal, The Montreal Museum of Fine Arts, 1967, No. 115.

37. *American Paintings*, II, p. 23.

247 *Mrs. John Champneys*, b. 1746 B.60.50
Jeremiah Theus, active ca. 1719–1774
Charleston, South Carolina, ca. 1765
Oil on canvas. H. 30 W. 25

Anne, daughter of George and Eleanor Livingston, was born in Port Island, South Carolina. At the age of 17 she married John Champneys (1743–1820) of Charleston. During the Revolution, loyalist Champneys and his wife were forced to flee to England, and it is believed that Anne Champneys died sometime during their absence from Charleston. This portrait descended in the family of her daughter, Sarah Champneys Tunno.

The painting is representative of Theus' Charleston work, a half-length figure in strong light against a dark background. The stiff posture and awkward right arm are also typical of Theus. Another sitter, *Mrs. Samuel Prioleau, II*, wears the identical silver dress, and two other subjects, *Mrs. Barnard Elliot*,

Jr., and *Jane Cuthbert*, wear dresses trimmed with ermine and pearls.[38]

38. Middleton, pp. 96, 67, 125.
REFERENCES. Middleton, p. 123.

248   *Unknown Boy*   B.54.31
        John Singleton Copley, 1738–1815
        Boston, ca. 1758–1760
        Oil on canvas. H. 50 W. 41

Although the subject of this portrait has not been identified, he has traditionally been thought to be a member of the Hancock family.[39] The picture is an early Copley work and dates from the late 1750's, the elegant nonchalance of pose reflecting English rococo prototypes. Both the pose and palette — cool blue waistcoat, grey coat — recall Copley's *Thaddeus Burr*.[40]

Originally Copley intended the subject to hold a large book under his right arm but later altered the composition to include the battledore and shuttlecock, continuing the tradition of portraying children with toys or pets.

39. The painting descended in the Sheafe family of Portsmouth, New Hampshire. Dorothy Quincy, who married John Hancock, was the aunt of Mary Quincy, who married Jacob Sheafe (1745–1820). After the death of John Hancock in 1793 Mrs. Hancock married Colonel James Scott. In 1809, once again a widow, she went to live in the Wentworth House in Portsmouth. Following her death the Sheafes lived there. Whether the subject here is a Quincy, a Sheafe or a Hancock is not known.
40. Prown, I, Fig. 91. Anything more than a stylistic connection between this portrait and that of *Thaddeus Burr* is not clear, but it is interesting to note that during the early months of the Revolution Dorothy Quincy and Lydia Hancock took refuge with Thaddeus Burr at his home in Fairfield, Connecticut (Parker and Wheeler, p. 156).
REFERENCES. Parker and Wheeler, p. 191; Prown, I, p. 32, Fig. 88.
EXHIBITIONS. Portsmouth, New Hampshire, Portsmouth Atheneum; Boston, The Old Boston Museum.

249   *Mrs. Paul Richard*, 1700–1773 (*opposite*)   B.54.18
        John Singleton Copley, 1785–1815
        New York, ca. 1771
        Oil on canvas. H. 50 W. 39½

Elizabeth Gorland Richard was a wealthy widow when Copley painted her portrait during his 1771 sojourn in New York. Her husband, Paul Richard (d. 1756), a prominent New York merchant, was mayor of the City of New York from 1725 to 1739. As the Richards had no children, much of their estate was left to a nephew, Theophilact Bache, and this painting descended in the Bache and Bleeker families of New York.

The portrait, a rococo *portrait d'apparat*, is one of Copley's eminently successful studies of elderly women. In his mature American style, the subject is dramatically lighted against a dark background. Mrs. Richard is seated in a green damask-covered open armchair that appears in several other portraits of older women.[41]

41. Prown, I, Figs. 179, 275.
REFERENCES. Parker and Wheeler, p. 162, Pl. 110; James T. Flexner, *John Singleton Copley*, Cambridge, 1948, p. 57, Pl. 15; Prown, I, p. 81, Fig. 287.
EXHIBITIONS. Boston, Museum of Fine Arts, *John Singleton Copley 1738–*

1815, 1938, p. 27; Des Moines, The Art Center, *Master Painters*, 1951, No. 12.

250 *Elizabeth Byles Brown*, 1737–1763   B.54.21
John Singleton Copley, 1738–1815
Boston, 1763
Pastel crayons on paper. H. 17½ W. 14½

Elizabeth Byles Brown was the daughter of the Reverend Mather Byles and mother of artist Mather Brown (1761–1831). Her husband Gawen Brown was a clockmaker. Copley painted both this pastel and a larger oil portrait in 1763.[42] The pastel descended in the family of Elizabeth's niece, Rebecca Byles Almon.

In early 1762 Copley wrote the Swiss pastelist, Jean-Etienne Liotard, requesting a set of crayons; the following year he made several pastel portraits, including this one.[43] The composition was derived from a 1761 English mezzotint of *Maria, the Countess of Coventry*, by Thomas Frye.[44] Copley simplified the prototype, eliminating some of the elaborate jewelry, but retained the ermine-trimmed cloak. The pastel seems to have been the basis for the oil portrait, which further simplified the original composition. The Bayou Bend picture is signed, *I S* (in a monogram) *C del.*, and dated, *1763*.

42. Formerly at Yale University Art Gallery (Prown, I, Fig. 111). *Antiques*, December 1972, p. 957.
43. Prown, I, p. 37.
44. Prown, I, Fig. 109.
REFERENCES. Perkins, p. 17; Bolton, No. 8; Bayley, p. 181; Parker and Wheeler, p. 218, Pl. 126; Prown, I, p. 37, Fig. 110; *XVII & XVIII Century American Furniture and Paintings*, p. 122.
EXHIBITIONS. New York, Metropolitan Museum of Art, *An Exhibition of Paintings by John Singleton Copley*, 1937, No. 7; Boston, Museum of Fine Arts, *John Singleton Copley 1738–1815*, 1938, No. 14.

251 *Sarah Henshaw*, 1732–1822   B.54.25
John Singleton Copley, 1738–1815
Boston, ca. 1770
Pastel crayon on paper. H. 24 W. 17¾

Sarah Henshaw of Boston, daughter of Joshua and Elizabeth Bill Henshaw, married her first cousin, Joseph Henshaw, in 1758.[45] Although Copley made a number of pastel portraits during the late 1760's, by about 1770 he seems to have abandoned the medium. His portrait of *Sarah Henshaw*, therefore, is a late pastel in his mature style.

The subject's fur-trimmed dress and scarf recall Copley's pastels of *Mrs. Joseph Green* and *Ruth Tufts*.[46] The introduction of a hand echoes the pastel portrait of *Mrs. Henry Hill*.[47] Although the compositional source has not been identified, a circa 1770 allegorical print of Catherine McCaulay, *In the Character of a Roman Matron*, shows Mrs. McCaulay assuming a similar pose and wearing a scarf over her head.[48] Either this print or another portraying a lady in Roman attire was the probable inspiration for Copley's pastel.

45. Copley also painted a portrait of *Joseph Henshaw*, as well as Sarah's brother and sister-in-law, Mr. and Mrs. Joshua Henshaw (Prown, I, Figs. 306, 307, 308).
46. Prown, I, Figs. 216, 239.

47. Prown, I, Fig. 243.

48. Claire Gilbride Fox, "Catherine MacCaulay and Eighteenth Century Clio," *Winterthur Portfolio*, Vol. 4, The Henry Francis du Pont Winterthur Museum, 1968, p. 133.

REFERENCES. Perkins, p. 71; Bayley, p. 142; Bolton, No. 28; Parker and Wheeler, p. 225; *XVII & XVIII Century American Furniture and Paintings*, p. 124.

EXHIBITIONS. Boston, Museum of Fine Arts, 1919; Boston, Museum of Fine Arts, *John Singleton Copley 1738–1815*, 1938, p. 24, No. 43.

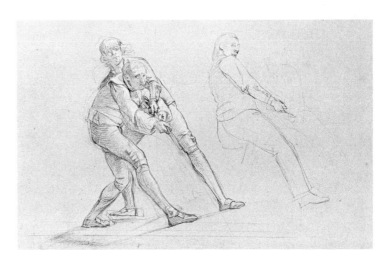

252 *Study for the Siege of Gibraltar* B.54.29
John Singleton Copley, 1738–1815
London, England, ca. 1785–1786
Black & white chalk on gray-blue paper. H. 14 W. 22½

From 1779 until 1782 Spanish and French naval forces besieged the British garrison at Gibraltar. On September 13, 1782, the siege was broken by English bombardment of enemy vessels, causing a fire and two subsequent cataclysmic explosions. This important victory against Britain's traditional enemies seized the imagination of the public, and, the following spring, Copley was commissioned by the Corporation of the City of London to paint the historic event. He decided to depict the break of dawn when the rising sun revealed the British garrison observing the scene of fire, death and destruction. The finished canvas was to be eighteen by twenty feet. Between 1782 and 1791 Copley labored on this immense project and, in the process, made many preparatory drawings. This is one of the studies for the lower left-hand portion of the painting where men rescue their comrades from a floundering boat. It and the three following drawings were sold from the library of Copley's son, Lord Lyndhurst, to Edwin Basil Tupp. They later were purchased by Copley's granddaughter, Elizabeth Amory, and her family and were subsequently given to a servant in whose family they descended.

REFERENCES. *Lyndhurst*, No. 661; Comstock, "Drawings of John Singleton Copley," p. 104; Prown, II, p. 445, Fig. 505.

253 *Study for the Siege of Gibraltar* B.54.30
John Singleton Copley, 1738–1815
London, England, ca. 1785–1786
Black & white chalk on gray-blue paper.
H. 23⅛ W. 14½

Here, from several angles, Copley has observed the action of a figure on a cannon in one of the long boats.

REFERENCES. *Lyndhurst*, No. 661; Comstock, "Drawings of John Singleton Copley," p. 107; Prown, II, p. 449, Fig. 512.

254 *Study for the Siege of Gibraltar* B.54.28
John Singleton Copley, 1738–1815
London, England, ca. 1785–1786
Black & white chalk on gray-green paper.
H. 14¼ W. 23

A hand reaches out to grasp the wrist of the nude figure at the left. Both the pose and the theme of rescue echo Copley's earlier *Brook Watson and the Shark*.[49] The two men at the right

pull in an oar. Above, the spontaneous line of a writhing nude figure is in sharp contrast to the more finished state of the other figures within the drawing.

49. The 1778 original is at the National Gallery, Washington (Prown, II, Fig. 371). A later vertical version dated 1782 is at the Detroit Institute of Arts (Prown, II, Fig. 373), and a copy of that painting is in the Bayou Bend Collection (B.56.16).
REFERENCES. *Lyndhurst*, No. 661; Prown, II, p. 45, Fig. 532.

255 *Study for the Siege of Gibraltar* B.54.27
John Singleton Copley, 1738–1815
London, England, ca. 1786–1787
Pencil, black & white chalk on gray-blue paper.
H. 14¼ W. 22½

This and one other sketch study the figure of the Hon. Lieutenant Colonel Lindsey, a bonneted and kilted officer at the far right of the finished painting.[50] The figures at the left of this drawing are further studies for rescue scenes.

50. Prown, II, Fig. 554.
REFERENCES. *Lyndhurst*, No. 661; Prown, II, p. 453, Fig. 553.

256 *Study for William Murray,* B.54.26
First Earl of Mansfield
John Singleton Copley, 1738–1815
London, England, 1782–1783
Pencil, black & white chalk on gray-blue paper.
H. 12¼ W. 19½

A skilled draughtsman, Copley prepared numerous sketches for his historical paintings (Nos. 252–255) and occasionally in planning his portraits. This sketch is one of several the artist contemplated for the 1783 oil portrait of *William Murray, Earl of Mansfield*.[51] The seated figure of Murray, to the left, comes closest to the final composition.

51. Prown, II, Figs. 429, 430, 432–435.
REFERENCES. *Lyndhurst*, No. 670.

257 *Noah Sacrificing* B.67.25
Benjamin West, 1738–1820
London, England, ca. 1780
Pen, ink, sepia wash on paper. H. 4¼ W. 8½

In 1780 George III commissioned Benjamin West to paint a series of murals on revealed religion for his new chapel at Windsor Castle. The paintings, thirty-six in number, were to be divided equally between the Old and New Testaments. West made some preparatory sketches, and John Galt, the artist's earlier biographer, quotes him as saying, "I arranged several subjects from the four Dispensations. His Majesty was pleased to approve the Arrangement."[52] Under the heading of the first Dispensation, Galt listed a 1780 painting entitled *Noah and his Family Sacrificing*.[53] The spontaneous Bayou Bend drawing is undoubtedly a preparatory sketch for the painting.

52. John Galt, *The Life Studies and Work of Benjamin West* (1820, Scholars, Facsimiles and Reprints, Gainesville, Florida, 1960), p. 209; The Dispensations, Pre-Abrahamic, Abrahamic, Mosaic and Christian,

are the four epochs of Christian salvation. Noah represents the Pre-Abrahamic period.

53. Galt, p. 209; *Noah Sacrificing* was listed in 1825 (*Catalogue of Pictures and Drawings by Benjamin West*, London, C. H. Reynell, 1825, p. 30). The author is indebted to Mrs. Clifford Vernarde for these references.

258 *Conversion of Onesimus*   B.67.26
Benjamin West, 1738–1820
London, England, ca. 1780
Pen, ink, sepia wash on paper. H. 5 W. 7½

This somewhat more finished drawing, another of West's series for George III, is based on the Epistle of St. Paul to Philemon written from prison in Rome. In it the apostle described the conversion of his fellow prisoner, a runaway slave named Onesimus, and requested that his master Philemon receive him as a Christian brother. West has depicted the moment of conversion, Onesimus kneeling with crossed arms receiving the blessing of Paul. The third figure, Epaphras draws back in awe of the wondrous event. Although this epistle to Philemon is a minor New Testament document, it has special significance to scholars since the converted Onesimus is thought later to have become Bishop of Ephesis and is believed to have gathered together the Epistles of St. Paul thus forming the nucleus of the New Testament. His conversion, therefore, was a particularly important event in the history of "revealed religion." As a New Testament story it was a part of the fourth dispensation.

259 *Girl with a Toy Horse*   B.55.15
Charles Willson Peale, 1741–1824
London, England, ca. 1768
Oil on canvas. H. 36 W. 28

In 1767 Charles Willson Peale went to London to study under Benjamin West and, the following year, painted this portrait of an unknown subject.[54] Rather than reflecting the grand neoclassical style, this early Peale is in the spirit of the English rococo conversation piece. Peale has carefully recorded all the details of a contemporary interior. Repeated rectangles of the fireplace, coal grate, mantel tablet, horse's legs, chair seat and leg are worked together in geometric alliteration. With a touch of humor, Peale repeats the entire picture over the fireplace. The subject wears a silver-gray dress with a pink underskirt. However, glowing coals in the grate, the rug's orange pattern and the red shoes provide bright visual accents in an otherwise subdued color scheme. In 1767 Copley exhibited his *Young Lady with a Bird and Dog* for the Society of Artists.[55] The following year the Society held a special exhibition to celebrate the visit of King Christian VIII of Denmark. Peale's offering to that exhibit, *Portrait of a Girl*, is probably this painting.[56] The parallels between this and Copley's picture suggest that Peale may have been responding to the work of his American friend.

54. The broad face of the subject is similar to that of Peale's circa 1767 diary sketch of a laughing boy (Sellars, p. 54).
55. At the Toledo Museum (Prown, I, Fig. 164).
56. Sellars, p. 71.

260 *Self-Portrait with Wife* (Rachel)   B.60.49
   and Daughter (Angelica Kauffmann)
   Charles Willson Peale, 1741–1824
   Philadelphia, ca. 1788
   Oil on canvas. H. 35 W. 27¼

During his career, Charles Willson Peale painted not only a number of penetrating self-portraits but also several conversation pieces of various Peale family members. Here the two have been subtly combined. The strong ties of familial devotion, seen in earlier works such as the *Peale Family Group*, are implicit in this delightful painting of the artist, Rachel Brewer Peale (1744–1790) and Angelica Kauffmann Peale (1775–1790).[57] Angelica, who painted well as a little girl, reaches like a playful muse to guide her father's brush. Peale has painted the picture in the clear, crisp manner that he adopted in the 1780's.

After the birth of Rosalba Carriera Peale in 1788, Rachel began to suffer ill health and never fully recovered before her death in 1790. Angelica, who was born in 1776, appears here to be about twelve. Angelica's age and Rachel's apparent well-being suggest that this portrait was painted about 1788.

57. Sellars, Fig. 20.
REFERENCE. Sellars, Pl. VI.

261 *Pleasure Party by a Mill*   B.62.16
   James Peale, 1749–1831
   Philadelphia, ca. 1790
   Oil on canvas. H. 26 W. 40

This pastoral scene of Bloomsbury, New Jersey, is one of the earliest major American landscapes. Although it was once attributed to Charles Willson Peale, a sketchbook of James Peale's, containing a drawing and supplementary sketches of the site, offers strong evidence of authorship by the less famous brother.[58] This attribution is supported by a comparison with both *James Peale and His Family* (1795)[59] and a series of paintings by James illustrating events of the Revolutionary War, particularly *Allen McLane and the British Dragoons* (1803).[60] In the foreground of each of these paintings, mullen and other varieties of plants are distinctively depicted in the manner of a detailed botanical study.

Unquestionably, there is a stiff quality about these works. With few exceptions, all are a curious combination of the eighteenth century conversation piece and topographical studies. Not without charm and pleasantly warm coloration, *Pleasure Party by a Mill* is typical of Peale's early landscapes where the picture tends to suffer, compositionally, from too accurate an observation of reality. Thus, despite the broad expanse of pinkish-blue sky, which has nineteenth century romantic overtones, this work lacks the cohesive effect of his paintings of the 1820's.[61] The members of the picnic party, dressed in colonial period costumes, are unidentified, but an early history of the town describes the prominent buildings along the Musconetcong Creek as an ironworks and a grist mill. The first stone house on the hill to the right was the tavern.

58. The only extant sketchbook by James Peale is in the American Philosophical Society Library, Philadelphia. It bears the notations, *Oct* and *No. 5*. The earliest date found in the book is 1786, while the latest is 1801.

59. The Pennsylvania Academy of Fine Arts, Philadelphia.

60. *Antiques*, December 1954, p. 493.

61. Peale's later landscapes such as *Wissahickon* (Swarthmore College) reflected the growing sophistication of landscape art and the possible influence of such artists as Francis Guy (1760–1820) and Thomas Doughty (1793–1856).

262 *Mrs. Mary Cuthbert*   B.61.64
Henry Benbridge, 1743–1812
South Carolina, ca. 1770–1775
Oil on canvas. H. 36 W. 31½

This portrait descended in the Cuthbert family of South Carolina, but the identity of the sitter is not certain. Her age and costume, nevertheless, suggest she may be Mary Hazard Wigg, who married Doctor James Cuthbert (1716–1794). In both pose and technique the portrait bears a striking similarity to that of *Mrs. Benjamin Simmons, II*, painted by Benbridge in the early 1770's.[62] The garb and pose also recall several other elderly Charleston subjects, particularly *Margaret Miles Hartley* and *Heriot Cunningham Cooke*.[63]

Mrs. Cuthbert is painted with the clarity of line that marks Benbridge's neoclassical style. The rather large head, combined with the small body and arms, are typical of the artist's work; but it is as a study of an elderly indomitable lady that the picture is particularly successful.

62. Gardner and Feld, p. 65.

63. Robert G. Stewart, *Henry Benbridge (1743–1812): American Portrait Painter*, Washington, D.C., Smithsonian Institution Press, 1971, Nos. 31, 72.

REFERENCES. Robert G. Stewart, No. 14; Middleton, p. 126.

263 *Robert Livingston, b. 1733*   B.72.117

Gilbert Stuart, 1755–1828
Ireland, ca. 1789
Oil on canvas. H.30 W.25
Gift of Mr. and Mrs. Harris Masterson

Stuart portrayed this Irish gentleman in the facile mature style that he developed during his years in London. Painted in Dublin, the portrait is closely related to that of *John Richardson*, which dates from the previous year.[64] Both are relatively early examples of Stuart's departure from the large scale and rich backgrounds of his London portraits to the untroubled, calm, neoclassical compositions of his American work.

An inscription on the back reads *Robertus Livingston/ Anno et 56/1789*. The painting is in its original gilt frame which bears the framemaker's label, *Jackson/No. 5/Essex Bridge/Dublin*.

64. *Gilbert Stuart*, No. 15.

EXHIBITIONS. Dublin, National Portrait Gallery of Ireland; Ulster Museum; and Dublin, National Portrait Gallery, *Irish Portraits from 1660–1800*, 1969–1970, No. 89.

264 *George Washington, 1732–1799*   B.60.46

Gilbert Stuart, 1755–1828
Philadelphia, ca. 1795–1796
Oil on canvas. H.30¼ W.25¼

In 1795, while in Philadelphia, Gilbert Stuart first painted George Washington from life. That picture, which shows the right-hand side of Washington's face, was ordered by John Vaughan (No. 265) for his father, Samuel Vaughan (1720–1802), who was living in London.[65] The portrait was received with such enthusiasm that Stuart began making replicas on commission; some seventeen are known today.[66] They vary in background and minor details. This example is similar to the prototype, differing only in the breadth of face and type of jabot.

The portrait originally belonged to William Patterson (1752–1835) of Baltimore and descended through his granddaughter, Alice, who married William Hall Harris.

65. *Antiques*, October 1972, p. 661.

66. The finest and best known are at the National Gallery, Washington, D.C. (*Gilbert Stuart*, No. 27); the Metropolitan Museum, New York (Gardner and Feld, pp. 85, 87); and Winterthur (*Antiques*, November 1971, p. 767).

265 *John Vaughan, 1756–1842* (opposite) B.61.55

Gilbert Stuart, 1755–1828
Philadelphia, ca. 1795
Oil on canvas. H.30 W.25

John Vaughan was the fourth son of Samuel and Sarah Hallowell Vaughan. From 1779–1781 he served as Benjamin Franklin's secretary while the latter was in France and, in 1782, came to Philadelphia, bringing letters of introduction from Franklin. In Philadelphia, Vaughan became acquainted with the leaders of the infant nation, including Washington and Jefferson.

In 1795 he commissioned Gilbert Stuart to paint the life portrait of George Washington, now known as the Vaughan-type Washington (No. 264). Later, Vaughan was instrumental in passing to Jefferson intelligence that led to initiating negotiations for the Louisiana Purchase. Vaughan was a founder of the American Philosophical Society and for years served as its secretary.[67] The Bayou Bend picture descended in the family of his brother, Benjamin, of Hallowell, Maine.

Vaughan's portrait is executed with the luminosity of color, glowing flesh tones and spontaneous application of paint that mark Stuart at his finest. The composition — a calm, unmoving bust-length figure against a plain background — was used also in the *Washington* portrait and is one that occurs frequently in Stuart's *oeuvre*.

67. The Society commissioned Thomas Sully to paint Vaughan's portrait in 1823, and that painting and another, *Samuel Vaughan* by Robert Edge Pine, are in the Society's collection (*Antiques*, November 1973, p. 879, Fig. 3, and Color Pl. IV, facing p. 886). Another Sully of Vaughan is at Bowdoin College (*Antiques*, November 1973, p. 862, Fig. 8). REFERENCES. Lawrence Park, *Gilbert Stuart: An Illustrated Descriptive List of His Works*, Vol. 2, New York, William Edwin Ridge, 1926, p. 778. EXHIBITIONS. Boston, Museum of Fine Arts, 1880.

266 *Unknown Man* B.59.52

Charles Balthazar Julien Févret de Saint-Mémin, 1770–1852
Baltimore, ca. 1804–1809
Crayon on paper. H.21½ W.15½

Although the subject of this portrait has been identified as Alexander Smith of Baltimore, no such name appears in the city *Directories* between 1804–1809, the years that Saint-Mémin worked there.[68] There is, however, a remarkable resemblance between this drawing and a Saint-Mémin miniature thought to portray David Conyngham Stewart (1775–ca. 1820).[69] The profile, dress and hairstyle are identical.

Although Saint-Mémin used a physiognotrace to create his neoclassical portraits, the inclusion of realistic detail masks that mechanical process. While blue paper was occasionally employed, most of his drawings, including this example, were made on pink paper. The black and gold églomisé matting is original.

68. The Smith identification was based on close similarity to a small medallion watercolor with reverse profile (E. Dexter, *The Saint-Memin Collection of Portraits . . . compiled from authentic and original sources*, New York, E. Dexter, 1862, No. 390).

69. J. Hall Pleasants, "Saint-Mémin Watercolor Miniatures," *The Walpole Society Notebook*, Portland, Maine, Anthoensen Press, 1947, p. 60. EXHIBITIONS. New York, The Metropolitan Museum of Art, on loan from John Hill Morgan.

267   *USS Wasp Sinking HMS Reindeer*   B.62.1.3

John Christian Schetky, 1778–1874
England, ca. 1820
Watercolor on paper. H.15 W.19¼

On May 1, 1814, the *USS Wasp* sailed from Portsmouth, New Hampshire, bound for the English channel to harass British shipping. Her mission was conducted with such success that on the twenty-eighth of June three enemy vessels appeared to do battle with her. The *Wasp* managed to elude two of the pursuers, but the third closed, showed her colors and opened fire. After a battle of several hours the enemy, *HMS Reindeer*, surrendered. Having transferred some of the wounded to a neutral Portuguese vessel, Captain Blakely of the *Wasp* sank the *Reindeer* and sailed to L'Orient with the remainder of her crew.[70] Here the artist has combined the transfer and sinking in this meticulously rendered watercolor.

John Christian Schetky, an English marine painter, worked in the traditions of Dutch seventeenth century marine artists. He taught drawing at the Royal Naval College at Portsmouth and later held a similar post in the East India College at Addiscombe. Schetky was appointed painter in watercolors to William, Duke of Clarence, and was marine painter to George IV, William IV and Queen Victoria. Although he never visited America, he did exhibit at the Pennsylvania Academy in 1821. This watercolor is one of a set made by Schetky illustrating naval engagements during the War of 1812.[71]

70. J. Lossing Benson, *The Pictorial Field-Book of the War of 1812*, New York, Harper & Brothers, 1869, p. 979.

71. Three others, *HMS Avon vs. USS Wasp, A British Man-O-War* and *HMS Avon* are in the Bayou Bend Collection. All are in their original frames which bear the maker's label, *Bowling and Brown, 464 Strand, London*. A handwritten description of each scene is also affixed to the back of the frame. Three more of the series were available at the time these were acquired for Bayou Bend. All of these naval engagements were reproduced in print form. Other examples of Schetky's work are in the collection of Paul Mellon.

The leopard with the harmless kid laid down,
And not one savage beast was seen to frown.

The wolf did with the lambkin dwell in peace,
His grim carnivrous nature there did cease;

The lion with the fatling on did move,
A little child was leading them in love;

When the great PENN his famous treaty made
With INDIAN chiefs beneath the elm tree's shade.

268   *The Peaceable Kingdom*   B.54.1
       Edward Hicks, 1780–1849
       Pennsylvania, ca. 1830–1835
       Oil on canvas. H. 17½ W. 23½

Edward Hicks, a Quaker preacher as well as sign and
coach painter, repeatedly depicted the *Peaceable Kingdom* in the
years between 1825 and his death in 1849. Most of the approximately one hundred versions known today include Penn's
Treaty. The theme is based on the eleventh chapter of "Isaiah"
where the prophet discusses the ultimate ideal of a peaceful
world. Because of the historical emphasis on peace as a principal
goal of the Society of Friends, Hicks' paintings held great ap-
peal to Quakers in many parts of America. The artist felt that
William Penn's holy experiment laid the seeds for fulfilling the
biblical prophecy of heaven on earth and, as such, was entirely
appropriate to be incorporated into his peace pictures. The
earliest examples, which depict the child with relatively few
small-scale animals, are based on a painting by Richard Westall,

R. A., which was reproduced in print form in a number of
Bibles and prayer books published during the 1820's.[72] The
treaty scene was based on H. B. Hall's engraving of the subject
by Benjamin West. This version, while similar to an oil on
wood at Yale, is almost identical to a slightly larger oil on
canvas belonging to the New York State Historical Association.[73] The lettering around the side is verse variations on the
biblical text. At the corner squares Hicks has painted the lamb
of God and the dove of peace, and the words *Innocence*, *Meekness*
and *Liberty*, in English, French, Latin and Greek.[74] This version
descended in a Pennsylvania family and traditionally belonged
to a friend of the artist, Amos Campbell of Newton, Bucks
County.

72. Alice Ford, *Edward Hicks: Painter of the Peaceable Kingdom*, Philadelphia, The University of Pennsylvania Press, 1952, p. 138.
73. Mary Black and Jean Lipman, *American Folk Painting*, New York
Clarkson N. Potter, Inc., 1966, Fig. 166; Ford, p. 140.
74. Another version of this type is at Swarthmore College (Ford,
p. xii).

269 *Oliver Hazard Perry, 1785–1819*   B.69.394
Samuel Waldo, 1783–1861
New York, ca. 1813
Oil on canvas. H. 24 W. 19½
Gift of Hirschl and Adler Galleries

In September 1813 Oliver Hazard Perry decisively defeated the British at the Battle of Lake Erie. His terse report has become immortal: "We have met the enemy and they are ours." Perry's victory seized the imagination of the American public, and overnight he became a popular hero.

Samuel Lovett Waldo, New York's leading portraitist, apparently painted Perry shortly after his gallant defeat of the enemy. The picture was stipple engraved by David Edwin (1776–1841) for the *Aneletic Magazine*, published in Philadelphia between 1813 and 1820. That engraving reveals that originally Perry's right hand was thrust into his coat; the present awkward thumb is a later addition. The painting echoes the style of Gilbert Stuart and recalls the composition of a contemporary Waldo at the Metropolitan Museum, New York.[75]

75. Gardner and Feld, p. 171.

270 *Unknown Woman*   B.67.37
Samuel Lovett Waldo, 1783–1861, and
William L. Jewett, 1789/1790–1874
New York, ca. 1830
Oil on wood panel. H. 36⅛ W. 28⅛

This elegant picture represents fashionable New York portraiture of the Waldo and Jewett partnership. Painterly colorism evidences the influence of Stuart on later American portraiture, while the costume suggests a date of about 1830. The pose and composition of this unsigned portrait are similar to several, and the book motif appears in two others.[76] The elegant seemingly boneless hand recalls that of Waldo's *Charles Addoms*.[77] This portrait is painted on a wood panel, a practice frequently employed by Waldo and Jewett.

76. Gardner and Feld, pp. 177, 179.
77. *American Paintings*, II, p. 131.

271 *Andrew Jackson, 1767–1845*   B.68.22
   Ralph E. W. Earl, ca. 1785–1838
   Tennessee, ca. 1835
   Oil on canvas. H.28⅝ W.22¼

   In 1816 Ralph E. W. Earl conceived the idea of recording
the heroes of the Battle of New Orleans (1815), and the following year he traveled to Nashville to paint Andrew Jackson.
While working there he met Mrs. Jackson's niece, Jane Caffery,
whom he married a year later.

   From that time on Earl's association with the Jackson
family became very intimate. After the death of Jackson's wife,
Rachel Donelson Jackson, the artist went to live with the President, first at the White House and later at the Hermitage. During that time he made numerous portraits of Andrew Jackson.
This example portrays a wise, strong elder statesman but, at the
same time, captures the sorrow and tragedy that overshadowed
Jackson's life after the death of his beloved wife. The large head,
with shock of gray hair, stands out dramatically against the dark
background. The face of Jackson, probably painted from memory, is similar to that in a full-length portrait painted about the
same time.[78] In composition the Bayou Bend portrait relates
closely to one at Yale.[79] The example here descended in the
Donelson family of Nashville.

   78. *The American Earls*, The University of Connecticut, The William
Benton Museum of Art, 1972, No. 21.
   79. *The American Earls*, No. 20.

272 *Mrs. John Earnest Poyas, 1769–1836*   B.67.32
   Samuel F. B. Morse, 1791–1872
   Charleston, South Carolina, ca. 1818
   Oil on canvas. H.29¾ W.23⅜

   An earlier portrait of *Catherine Smith Poyas*, daughter of
Henry and Elizabeth Ball Smith who lived at Goose Creek,
outside Charleston, had been painted by Theus when she was a
child.[80] After her marriage in 1785 to Dr. John Earnest Poyas
(1759–1824), she moved to Charleston where Morse painted
this portrait and that of *Dr. Poyas*, during December 1818 and
January 1819.[81]

   Morse had come to Charleston in late 1818 to spend the
first of four winters there. In the following February he wrote
his friend, Washington Allston, commenting on his remarkable
success: "I am painting from morning till night and have continued applications."

   Catherine Poyas is a bold color statement — her black
dress, stark white lace and bonnet against a pink and blue sunset
sky. The sleeves of her dress are trimmed with touches of red
embroidery. Stylistically, the portrait is similar to that of *Mrs.
Griffith*, painted circa 1820.[82]

   80. Middleton, p. 166.
   81. The Poyas portraits are included on Morse's list of works, now in
the Library of Congress, Washington, D.C.
   82. *American Paintings*, II, p. 110.

273 *Autumn in the Catskill Mountains* B.68.27

Thomas Cole, 1801–1848
New York, ca. 1825–1830
Oil on canvas. H. 28¼ W. 40

Lacking a history or civilization as old as that in England, France and Italy, nineteenth century Americans urgently searched for a sense of a national past and heritage. A common source of pride was found in the rugged, beautiful American landscape which provided a perfect foil to the historical and mythological subject matter of European painting. Thomas Cole, one of the great figures in early nineteenth century American landscape painting and a founder of the Hudson River School, sought to make his depictions of nature more than faithful reproductions of what he saw. His works often embodied philosophical conceptions with moral and religious overtones.

This painting, which is Claudian in its pastoral idealism, probably dates from the late 1820's and is, in fact, similar to another view of the Catskills, dated 1827.[83] Corroborating this early date is Cole's reliance here on a traditional system of zig-zag diagonals, reinforced by subtle changes in tonality, to construct the composition. In contrast, his later paintings often projected the feeling of the raw power of nature through more forceful and complex manipulation of staging and chiaroscuro.

83. Howard S. Merritt, *Thomas Cole*, Memorial Art Gallery of the University of Rochester, 1969, No. 10. The Bayou Bend painting is signed on a rock in the lower left-hand corner, *T. Cole*.

274 *Lydia Smith Russell*, 1786–1859 B.71.39

George P. A. Healy, 1813–1894
Boston, ca. 1845
Oil on canvas. H. 29¾ W. 25

Lydia, born in Taunton, Massachusetts, was the daughter of Barney Smith and his wife, Ann Otis. As a young woman Lydia Smith was educated in Paris and studied painting under both Gilbert Stuart and Benjamin West. In 1817 she married Jonathan Russell (1771–1832), former *chargé d'affaires* in Paris and London, Commissioner and signer of the Treaty of Ghent. At the time of their marriage, Russell was Minister to Sweden and Norway and later served one term in the United States Congress (1821–1823). Mrs. Russell is typical of the wealthy influential cosmopolitan Americans who made up Healey's clientele. Her portrait is painted with the facile fidelity that characterized Healey's work at the middle of the nineteenth century.

Henry Clay and John Quincy Adams, both of whom served with Jonathan Russell at Ghent, were painted by Healey for Louis Philippe's collection of American notables in 1845. Healy came to Boston in August of that year and remained there until 1848 before returning to France. Mrs. Russell's portrait relates to Healy's works of this period, and it is possible that she sat for him during this Boston interlude.

275 *Landscape* B.67.39
Hermann Lungkwitz, 1813–1891
Texas, 1862
Oil on canvas. H. 18¾ W. 24⅛

Hermann Lungkwitz, born in Halle an der Salle, Germany, went to Dresden in 1838 to study painting at the Akademie der Bildende Künste. After five years of tutelage under Ludwig Richter, he departed Dresden to make a sketching tour through the Alps; landscapes painted following this tour were brought with the artist when he emigrated to America in 1848.[84] He first settled at Fredericksburg, in the Texas hill country, and worked in that area until the Civil War, when he moved to San Antonio and entered the photography business. Later, in 1871, when Lungkwitz's brother-in-law became Land Commissioner, he moved to Austin and became photographer for the Commission.

Although a small number of city views are known, the major portion of Lungkwitz's *oeuvre* is landscape. He seems to have been fascinated with the wild terrain and cool streams of the hill country. Stark outcroppings of rock and twisted grey-green Texas trees frequently appear in his paintings. The precise rendering of these natural features reflects his Dresden training. Following the precepts of romantic art, people appear in small scale suggesting the frailty of humanity in the face of vast untamed nature.

This picture, signed *H. Lungkwitz* and dated *1862*, appears to have been painted about the time the artist moved from Fredericksburg to San Antonio. While the exact location of the scene is not known, it appears to be either the Pedernales or Guadalupe River.

84. Pinckney, p. 88.

276 *The Lost Child Returned* B.71.80
Albert Fitch Bellows, 1829–1883
Antwerp, Belgium, or Boston, 1859
Oil on canvas. H. 33 W. 48

Albert Fitch Bellows enjoyed great popularity as a landscape and genre artist during the 1850's, 1860's and 1870's, and his work reflected the taste of Victorian America. During the 1876 Centennial he painted *Sunday Afternoon in New England*, a picture intended as a sample of the rustic beauty of a colonial New England village.[85] Here in this narrative painting he depicts a sentimental drama filled with overtones which suggest the virtues of rural life and familial devotion. As if in a stage play, light falls on the protagonists — rescuer, child and mother. The composition of the figures is tightly structured and recalls such works of George Caleb Bingham (1811–1879) as *The Emigration of Daniel Boone*.[86] For several years after 1855, Bellows was studying in Antwerp. The buildings in the background, especially the stone Gothic church, suggest that the artist may have portrayed a European village. *The Lost Child Returned* was exhibited by Bellows at the Washington (D.C.) Art Association in 1859, and Henry Tuckerman's *Book of Artists* (1867) discusses Bellows' *Lost Child*.[87]

85. In 1883 the picture hung in the Chicago residence of Mr. Henry J.

Willing and apparently was important enough to be fully described (*Artistic Houses*, New York, Benjamin Blom, 1971, Vol. 2, Part I, p. 38). That painting is now in the Chicago Art Institute.

86. At Washington University, St. Louis, Missouri.

87. The Washington Art Association sponsored exhibits between 1856 and 1860 but was disbanded during the Civil War. The author is indebted to Mrs. Francis Lytz for this information.

277 *Victorian Bouquet* 71-21

Severin Roesen, active ca. 1848–1872
New York, ca. 1850–1855
Oil on canvas. H. 36⅛ W. 29
Museum Purchase, Agnes Cullen Arnold Endowment Fund

Victorian Bouquet stands as a perfect cultural and aesthetic document of mid-nineteenth century America. Scientific curiosity, concern with material prosperity, awe of technical mastery and the assimilation of European art and ideas that characterize this period are all embodied in this colorful still life.[88]

Severin Roesen, a German immigrant who had been a porcelain and enamel painter in Cologne, was among the more active still-life painters after 1850, working first in New York and then in Pennsylvania.[89] Roesen's compositions were strongly influenced by the work of seventeenth century Dutch still-life masters like Jan van Huysum (1682–1749) and Rachel Ruysch (1664–1750).[90] His indebtedness to his predecessors included the use of certain objects or props in painting after painting — a bird's nest with three eggs, a heavy grey marble slab, a thin-stemmed glass, and selectively rearranged quantities of glass-surfaced fruits and vibrantly colored flowers. Further, he borrowed the technique of displaying the pyramidal arrangement of flowers and fruit against a contrasting dark background or within a niche. The artist's early paintings, like this one, have a clarity of organization and form which succumbed, after about 1860, to an incredibly overcrowded profusion of objects and detail. Yet, it was probably Roesen's unsophisticated clientele who catalyzed this change, equating quantity with quality. Undoubtedly they also appreciated his tight and draughtsmanlike style, which well suited the pragmatic American preference for super-realism and illusionistic attention to detail.

88. *Victorian Bouquet* is discussed at greater length in the *Bulletin*, The Museum of Fine Arts, Houston, Vol. 3, No. 4, June 1972, ill. cover, pp. 42–45.

89. The mysterious Roesen has been the subject of a recent intensive re-examination and research project. The published studies are: Maurice Mook, "Severin Roesen, The Williamsport Painter," *Lycoming College Magazine*, Vol. 25, No. 6, June 1972, pp. 33–42; Maurice Mook, "Severin Roesen and His Family," *The Journal of the Lycoming County Historical Society*, Vol. 3, No. 2, Fall 1972, pp. 8–12; Maurice Mook, "Severin Roesen: Also the Huntington Painter," *Lycoming College Magazine*, Vol. 26, No. 6, June 1973, pp. 13–18, 23–30.

90. The influence seems to have been an indirect one through a contemporary of Roesen's, Johann Wilhelm Preyer (1803–1889).

Silver

278 Pine Tree Shilling   B.68.8

Robert Hull and John Sanderson, active ca. 1652–1683
Boston, ca. 1652–1683
D. I

The minting of coins was prohibited in the colonies, but during the Protectorate of Cromwell, John Hull and his partner Robert Sanderson were engaged by the General Court of Massachusetts to establish a mint. Between 1652 and 1683 they produced the famous series of pine, oak and willow coins.[1] The design, with its beaded ring around the edge, was chosen to discourage the practice of "clipping," the removal of a small piece of silver from a coin.

1. The willow tree coins were minted beginning in 1652; the oak tree version, 1662; the famous pine tree coins, 1663. Although Hull and Sanderson minted the coins, it is thought that Joseph Jenckes, an iron founder, cut the die for the pine tree shilling (Flynt and Fales, p. 37).

279   Mug   B.69.119

Peter Van Dyck, 1684–1751
New York, 1705–1740
MARK: To left of handle and to right of handle.
H. 3¾ D. (of base) 3½ D. (of lip) 3-1/6

While cann and mug were apparently interchangeable terms in the eighteenth century, today a mug is usually differentiated from a cann by straight and slightly tapering, rather than curved, sides. New York taste favored straight-sided drinking vessels long after tulip-shaped bodies were in use elsewhere. The earliest mugs had flat strap handles, here embellished by graduated rat-tail beading and a serrated terminal.[2]

2. Two similar mugs by Van Dyck are the property of the First Presbyterian Church, Southampton, New York (Halsey, No. 123).

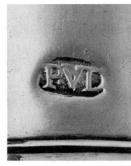

280   Mug   B.69.92

Peter Oliver, 1682–1712
Boston, ca. 1710
MARK: To left of handle and on base.
H. 4¼ D. (of base) 3⅝ D. (of lip) 3-1/6

Peter Oliver's short career is documented by less than a dozen known pieces of silver. This mug, plain except for a high midband and simple arms engraved on the body, exemplifies the early Boston type. It is also one of the earliest instances of the use of the hollow scroll handle on American mugs. One should note the existence of a mug with identical handle, base molding and armorial cartouche (the arms are different) by John Edwards.[3] A teapot by Nathaniel Hurd, at Winterthur, bears the same arms, identified as those of the Howard family.[4]

3. Hammerslough, Vol. 3, p. 21; it has been suggested that both Oliver and Edwards apprenticed with Jeremiah Dummer (Buhler, pp. 95, 121). The Hammerslough example has no midband.

4. Fales, *Winterthur Museum*, No. 28. The initials *A/I*M* are on the mug's handle.

281   Mug   B.61.54

William Cowell, 1682/3–1736
Boston, 1710–1720
MARK: Initials in a conforming shield to left of handle and
surname in semiscript on the base.
H. 4½   D. (of base) 3¾   D. (of lip) 3¾

This example represents a slight variation on the Peter
Oliver mug (No. 280).[5] Although the surname mark was used
by both Cowell and his son, its appearance here and on a tankard, together with the documented shield mark, identifies this
mug as the work of William Cowell, Sr.[6]

5. The unidentified initials *D/SC* and *HM* appear respectively on the
handle and base.

6. The tankard is owned by the First Church in Newton, Massachusetts.

282   Cann   B.61.18

Jacob Hurd, 1702/03–1758
Boston, 1725–1740
MARK: To left of handle.
H. 5 1/16   D. (of base) 3 5/16   D. (of lip) 3¼

Tulip or pear-shaped canns first appeared in America
about 1720. Decidedly bulbous and bottom-heavy at first, they
became, by mid-century, more attenuated and graceful. The
baroque coat of arms is ascribed to John Green of Charlestown,
Massachusetts.[7] The Hurd touchmark used on this cann is one
of six known. Its earliest dated use is on beakers of 1728 made
for the Second Church of Christ in Hingham, while the last
documented use is on a ring of 1740.[8]

7. While the cann cannot presently be traced to John Green, the Green
family in America did use this coat of arms. A similar crest appears on a
pair of casters made by Joseph Edwards, Jr. (1737–1783) for Joshua (1731–
1806) and Hannah Green of Boston (Buhler and Hood, No. 272). The
motto, which has been scratched out, reads *Nil Conscire Sibi*. The initials
MV are engraved on the base.

8. Buhler, p. 201.

283   Cann   B.69.99

Jacob Hurd, 1702/3–1758
Boston, 1725–1740
MARK: Full name in cartouche on base and surname in
semiscript in an ellipse to left of handle.
H. 4¼   D. (of base) 2⅞   D. (of lip) 2 13/16

While diminutive, this cann displays the consistently
high quality of craftsmanship that has earned Hurd a special
place among eighteenth century American silversmiths. The
source of the arms and crest, those of the Pierce family, appears
to be Logan's *Analogia Honorum* (1677), usually found bound
with Guillium's *Display of Heraldry* (1679).[9] An exact mate to
this cann is in the Detroit Institute of Arts.[10]

9. American families were often not very strict in their adoption or
use of arms, crests and mottoes. Logan's work lists the Pierce motto as
Devs Mihi Providebit, not *Devs Mihi Sol* as it appears on the cann.

10. Both the Detroit and Bayou Bend canns are listed in Hollis French,
Jacob Hurd and His Sons Nathaniel and Benjamin, Silversmiths, 1702–1781,
Cambridge, Massachusetts, 1939, p. 34, Nos. 60, 61.

284 Tankard

B.69.115

Jeremiah Dummer, 1645–1718
Boston, 1690–1700
MARK: To left of handle.
H. 6½ D. (of base) 5 D. (of lip) 4½

Such popular seventeenth and eighteenth century dinner beverages as beer, ale and hard cider seemed to call for more capacious drinking vessels; these larger and hinge-lidded versions of the mug or cann were called tankards. Early examples had flat lids, nearly vertical sides, cusped thumbpieces and a long v-shaped or rat-tail drop at the upper juncture of handle and body. Dummer, the first native-born and trained American silversmith whose work is extant, fashioned at least three other tankards with gadrooning on the lid.[11] Originally owned by John (1664–1738) and Experience Folger Swain (d. 1739) of Nantucket, Massachusetts, this tankard descended in successive family generations until acquired by Bayou Bend.[12]

11. South Parish, Portsmouth, New Hampshire; privately owned (Clarke, Pl. XVII); privately owned (*Antiques*, June 1953, p. 500).

12. Hannah Swain, daughter of John and Experience, married Thomas Gardner in whose family it descended. Engraved on the base are the initials of all the tankard's owners: *S/I*E* (contemporary with the piece); *THG–1740; TAG–1784; CAG–1817; ESG–1847; EB*MG–1875; ECSG–1905*. This tankard was exhibited (Phillips, No. 82, Fig. 30).

285 Tankard

B.63.71

Edward Winslow, 1669–1753
Boston, 1690–1700
MARK: On lid and to left of handle.
H. 6⅞ D. (of base) 5½ D. (of lip) 4⅝

Typical of early Massachusetts tankards are the dolphin-and-mask thumbpiece, the ribbed handle with scroll and the cut and applied sheet silver, or cut-card, decoration behind the lower handle juncture.[13] More universal was the use of a cast cherub's head for the handle terminal; the knop on the lid, however, is unique to this tankard.[14] The Payne family coat of arms is seen on the front of the barrel.[15]

13. On rare occasions, these features are found in Rhode Island tankards, suggesting possible master-apprenticeship, as well as commercial, ties (Hood, No. 76).

14. The only comparable flat-top lid finial is a low-relief molded rosette on a tankard by Jeremiah Dummer, Winslow's probable master (Clarke, Pl. XVI).

15. The tankard was owned, until purchased for Bayou Bend, by a collateral branch of the family of the original owners. Engraved on the base is *30:oz* and the later added script initials *CFD*.

286   Tankard   B.69.106

Isaac Anthony, 1690–1773
Newport, Rhode Island; Swansea, Massachusetts,
ca. 1727
MARK: In oval to left of handle and obliterated initial and
surname, colon between, in a rectangle, on handle.
H. 9½   D. (of base) 5⅝   D. (of lip) 4¾

Domed or "high-topped" tankards were made from
about 1715 to the end of the eighteenth century. The flame
finial on this example is an early instance of its use, while the
engraved handle terminal and leaf-decorated thumbpiece are
highly unusual. The coat of arms is believed to be that of the
Arnold family of Newport, Rhode Island.[16]

16. Engraved on the handle are the partially worn initials ?/B+E. The
inscription on the handle terminal reads, *March/ye 25th/1727*. On the
base the weight is recorded: *oz-d/31 = 4*.

287   Tankard   B.69.118

Peter Van Dyck, 1684–1751
New York, ca. 1710
MARK: On lid and twice to left of handle.
H. 7⅞   D. (of base) 6¼   D. (of lip) 3⅜

New York silver of the baroque period was treated in a
more opulent manner than was silver of the other colonies. The
use of elaborate cast and applied ornament, engraving and
stamped foliate basebands allowed imaginative silversmiths
such as Cornelius Kierstede (No. 302), Bartholomew Le Roux
and Peter Van Dyck a wide latitude of personal expression.
With a capacity of over two quarts, this tankard is one of the
largest known New York drinking vessels.[17] Made for the New
York-Bermuda merchant, Thomas (1671–1716?) and Sarah
Gibbs, family tradition states that the tankard was purchased in
1710 with all that was salvaged from the wreck of the Gibbs
ship on the English coast.[18] The use of an engraved ship on silver
tankards is not unique, however, and seems to parallel the use
of ships in paintings of the period (No. 235) as an iconographical reference to the owner's profession.[19]

17. One of Van Dyck's most impressive creations is a tankard now at
Yale University (Buhler and Hood, No. 587) which is identical in many
respects to the Bayou Bend example (*Antiques*, November 1946, p. 300;
Antiques, December 1966, p. 803).

18. The contemporary initials G/T*S and the date *1710* are engraved
on the base; a Gibbs coat of arms is on the barrel. The tankard was owned
by the Gibbs family until 1946.

19. For a similar use on a New York tankard, see Clara Louise Avery,
An Exhibition of Early New York Silver, New York, Metropolitan
Museum of Art, 1931, Figs. 51, 97.

288 Tankard B.69.102

Henricus Boelen, II, 1697–1755
New York, ca. 1730–40
MARK: To left of handle and to right of handle.
H. 7 D. (of base) 5½ D. (of lip) 4⅝

Flat-top tankards with straight tapered sides were preferred in New York long after fashion and stylistic changes
elsewhere dictated high-domed tops and curved bodies. Among
the distinctive New York features of this tankard is the French
coin, bearing a portrait of Louis XV and dated 1727, inset in
the lid.[20]

20. A similar tankard with an inset coin in the lid and with the initials
I H/I*M on the handle is in the Minneapolis Institute of Arts. The cast
handle terminal is a second type used by Boelen, however. Both the
Minneapolis and the Bayou Bend tankards are believed to have descended
in the Morris family of Morrisania, New York. The eighteenth century,
but not contemporary, script initials *VCN* on the body of the Bayou
Bend example may stand for a member of the Morris family. Euphemia
Morris married Captain Matthew Norris. The crest on the tankard is
also not contemporary. Engraved on the base is *31 oz. 15DWT*.

289 Tankard B.58.117

Johannis Nys, 1671–1734
New York (?), Philadelphia, Delaware, ca. 1700
MARKS: Three on lid near thumbpiece and one to right
of handle. H. 7¼ D. (of base) 5⅜ D. (of lip) 4⅞

Although Nys worked in the Philadelphia area, his use
of such characteristic New York features as applied stamped
basebands and cocoon or corkscrew-shaped thumbpieces indicates he was probably trained in that city. A nearly identical
tankard is in the Museum of Fine Arts, Boston.[21]

21. Buhler, No. 512. It is possible that the Bayou Bend tankard also
originally had a cast, applied cherub's head on the handle terminal. Another similar Nys tankard is the one made for James Logan which was
in the Philadelphia Museum exhibition (Prime, No. 307). The Bayou
Bend tankard was No. 309 in the same exhibition. The original weight
33 1/2 on. is scratched on the base.

290 Porringer B.69.116

Jeremiah Dummer, 1645–1718
Boston, 1680–1700
MARK: To right of handle on bowl and on back of
handle. H. 1¾ D. (of lip) 4⅝ L. (of handle) 2⅜

The earliest American porringers had straight sides and
flat bases, but as the form developed, it acquired curved sides,
a slightly domed base and an out-turned or everted lip. The
single handle and uncovered bowl is characteristic of all but a
few American porringers. While in England it is often referred
to as a bleeding bowl, in the colonies, the porringer seems to
have been used interchangeably with bowls of all types; generally, it served as a porridge or cereal bowl. More different
handle designs by Jeremiah Dummer are known than by any
other American silversmith.[22]

22. An identical porringer is at Historic Deerfield (Flynt and Fales,
No. 49); similar examples are at Phillips Academy, Addison Gallery of
American Art, Andover, Massachusetts; the Museum of Fine Arts,
Boston (Buhler, No. 17).

291　Porringer　　　　　　　　　　　　　　B.63.74

William Cowell, Sr., 1682–1736
Boston, 1705–1710
MARK: In center of bowl.
H. 1⅞ D. (of lip) 5³⁄₁₆ L. (of handle) 2⅝

All porringer handles were cast in sand molds. Late seventeenth and early eighteenth century examples were elaborately composed of various geometric shapes with initials of the owner(s) often placed on the face of the handle in an unpierced space near its juncture with the bowl. This porringer has the letters *B/R.H.* on the handle and is said to have belonged to the Butler family of Boston.[23]

23. A strap-handle mug of the same period by John Edwards (1671–1746) of Boston bears the same initials (formerly in the Phillip Hammerslough collection). The attribution of the *WC* mark on the Bayou Bend porringer has been the subject of some confusion and contradiction. It has been given both to William Cowell, Sr., and William Cross, 1658–? (Flynt and Fales, pp. 191–192; Buhler, p. 123). Cowell, however, is known to have used a distinctive "crown-crested" handle. Such an example in the Metropolitan Museum, New York, bears the same *WC* mark as that of the Bayou Bend porringer (Davidson, No. 116).

292　Porringer　　　　　　　　　　　　　　B.69.93

Samuel Vernon, 1683–1737
Newport, Rhode Island, 1705–1715
MARK: In bowl and on back of handle.
H. 2 D. (of lip) 5 L. (of handle) 2½

This handle is one of three known variations on the earliest geometric type used by Vernon.[24]

24. Porringers of nearly the same size and identical handle design are at Winterthur (Fales, *Winterthur Museum*, No. 58); two private collections (Carpenter, No. 119). Similar but variant types are illustrated (Carpenter, No. 120; Buhler and Hood, No. 455). An identical porringer by Edward Winslow (1669–1753) is in the Essex Institute (Fales, *Early American Silver*, p. 55). The Bayou Bend porringer has the initials *S/A*M* on the base and *S*S* on the handle.

293　Porringer　　　　　　　　　　　　　　B.69.101

John Edwards, 1671–1746
Boston, 1720–1746
MARK: Twice to left of handle and three times to right of handle. H. 2⅛ D. (of lip) 5¼ L. (of handle) 2⅜

The touchmark on this porringer was used by Edwards from approximately 1710 until the end of his career. The handle design is also a later type employed by Edwards and other silversmiths in all of the colonies from about 1720 on. The shape of the opening at the tip of the handle has led to the term keyhole-handled porringer. Another stylistic change is the double but separate arches at the base of the handle.[25]

25. The initials *B/IS* are in the front of the handle.

294 Porringer

John Dixwell, 1680–1725
Boston, 1715–1725
MARK: Back of handle.
H. 1⅞   D. (of lip) 4⅞   L. (of handle) 2⅜

Engraved with the initials *W/IM* on the handle, this porringer may have been owned by the Williams family of Portsmouth, New Hampshire.[26]

26. The handle has been repaired.

295 Porringer B.69.94

John Burt, 1692/93–1745/46
Boston, 1730–1745
MARK: On front of handle.
H. 1¾   D. (of lip) 5⅛   L. (of handle) 2¾

Burt was among the first Boston silversmiths to use a keyhole handle without arches.

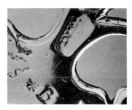

296 Porringer B.69.107

John Tanner, 1713–1785
Newport, Rhode Island, 1735–1785
MARK: Back of handle and left of handle.
H. 1 11⁄16   D. (of lip) 5 3⁄16   L. (of handle) 2⅝

The eventual evolution of the keyhole handle saw the arches at the base disappear entirely.[27]

27. Identical porringers are illustrated (Carpenter, No. 123; Buhler and Hood, No. 474). The initials *C/WM* are unidentified.

Porringer   B.56.33

Benjamin Burt, 1729–1805
Boston, 1750–1800
MARK: Front of handle.
H. 2 D. (of lip) 5 L. (of handle) 2¾

While many silversmiths used several different handle patterns, Benjamin Burt seems to have used only one, and it is identical to the handle on the porringer made by his father (No. 295). He also appears to have placed his touchmark consistently on the front of the handle.[28]

28. The inscription *Elizh Fellows* is on the handle. The base has the date *1730* on it, pointing out the fact that not all inscriptions can be taken at face value; Burt would have been one year old at the time.

298   Porringer   B.69.105

Samuel Minott, 1732–1803
Boston, 1755–1800
MARK: On back of handle.
H. 1¾ D. (of lip) 5⅛ L. (of handle) 2⅞

Initials are more common on porringers than are crests or arms. Although this porringer is thought to have descended in the Jennings family of Boston, use of the Wyvern crest by them has not been determined.[29]

29. The initials *I/D*I* are on the base. An identical porringer by Minott is at Historic Deerfield (Flynt and Fales, No. 76).

299   Porringer   B.61.20

Benjamin Bunker, 1751–1842
Nantucket, Massachusetts, 1775–1810
MARK: On back of handle and in center of bowl.
H. 2 D. (of lip) 4⅞ L. (of handle) 2¾

The similarity of marks used by silversmiths with the same initials often causes confusion. An identical porringer to the Bayou Bend example has been attributed to Benjamin Brenton (1710–1766) of Newport.[30] More recent scholarship suggests, however, that Bunker was responsible for both porringers.[31] The rarity of silver made by either silversmith adds to the uncertainty of attribution.

30. Carpenter, No. 125.

31. Flynt and Fales, pp. 164–165, 171. The marks taken from documented pieces of silver indicate that some of the examples now given to Brenton may have to be reattributed to Bunker. The initials *P/I*M* are unidentified.

300 Porringer B.69.114

Elias Pelletreau, 1726–1810
Southampton, New York, 1750–1780
MARK: On back of handle.
H. 2 D. (of lip) 4⅞ L. (of handle) 2⅛

The porringer, probably the most common hollowware form made by eighteenth century silversmiths, seems to have been ordered predominantly in pairs or sets.[32] The distinctive handle with three piercings was used almost exclusively by New York silversmiths.[33] The handle on this porringer was one of three designs used by Pelletreau.[34]

32. Out of 34 commissions for porringers recorded in Pelletreau's account books, all but nine were for two or more.

33. On rare occasions, silversmiths in Connecticut and Rhode Island, where New York influence was strong, used this type of handle (Buhler and Hood, Nos. 401, 463).

34. The unidentified initials B/M*E are on the back of the handle.

301 Porringer B.58.155

Joseph Richardson, 1711–1784
Philadelphia, ca. 1735
MARK: Twice on back of handle.
H. 1¾ D. (of lip) 5⅛ L. (of handle) 2⅝

Richardson is known to have made keyhole-handled porringers both with and without arches at the handle base.[35]

35. Buhler and Hood, No. 836. The unidentified script initials EWBA from MWAM are on the front of the bowl.

302 Two-Handled Bowl B.63.3

Cornelius Kierstede, 1675–1757
New York; Albany, New York; New Haven
Albany, ca. 1704–1706
MARK: Twice on rim.
H. 2³⁄₁₆ D. (of base) 2¼ D. (of bowl) 4½ W. 6¼

The rare two-handled bowl, inspired by Dutch examples, is a distinctive seventeenth and early eighteenth century New York-Albany form.[36] Thought to have been used originally for serving raisins in brandy, the bowls are characterized by their six panels or lobes, often ornamented with a raised or repoussé and chased floral motif. While the larger examples have cast s-scroll caryatid handles, the smaller bowls, as in this example, employ twisted silver wire or cut sheet.[37] An interesting feature of the bowl, also found on the lids of many New York tankards, is the French coin, dated 1693, and bearing the head of Louis XIV, inserted in the bottom. The initials M*G probably refer to Maria Pruyn Gerritsen (d. 1731) of Albany where Kierstede worked circa 1704–1706. The bowl descended directly in the family of the original owner until acquired by Bayou Bend.

36. For a full discussion of this form and its origins, see Antiques, October 1961. Approximately twenty bowls of this specific type are known.

37. A large bowl by Kierstede with caryatid handles is in the Metropolitan Museum, New York (Miller, New York Silversmiths, No. 27, Pl. XIV); another, without handles, is at Yale University, the Garvan Collection (Buhler and Hood, No. 329). The Bayou Bend bowl was included in the Museum of the City of New York exhibition (Miller, New York Silversmiths, No. 28). It is also illustrated and discussed, Antiques, October 1966, pp. 524–525.

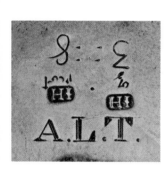

303 Spout Cup   B.69.108

John Burt, 1692/3–1745
Boston, 1725–1730
MARK: To right of handle.
H. 5½ D. (of base) 2⅞ D. (of lip) 2¹¹/₁₆

Apparently a New England form of the first half of the eighteenth century, spout cups vary greatly in details of design; the majority, however, like early chocolate pots, have their compressed tubular spouts and strap handles at right angles to each other.[38] An unusual feature of the Burt spout cup is the hinged cover, found on only one other example.[39] This rare silver form was probably used for feeding children and invalids.

38. The only two non-New England spout cups known are examples from New York and Philadelphia (*Antiques*, August 1943, pp. 74–75).
39. Buhler, No. 144. An added inscription, *Shaw/F.S.*, is on the base of the Bayou Bend cup, which was reputedly owned in Magnolia, Massachusetts.

304 Pepper Box   B.63.19

John Hastier, 1691–1771
New York, 1725
MARK: Twice on base.
H. 4⁷/₁₆ D. (of base) 2½ D. (of lip) 1⅞

Cylindrical and octagonally shaped pepper boxes, used for both pepper and mustard, were important articles of table silver until the mid-eighteenth century when they were replaced by the more stylish caster. Although casters were often made in sets of two or even three, pepper boxes seem to have been single items. It is unique, then, that this pepper box has two mates identical even to the weight and initials engraved on the base.[40] The block letters *A.L.T.* on the base may correspond to the intricate double cypher on the body.

40. Cleveland Museum of Art, Acc. No. 40.209; Bortman-Larus Collection (on loan, United States Department of State, Diplomatic Reception Rooms, Washington, D.C.). The original owner of the pepper boxes has not been identified. The inscribed weight is *3 oz.= 8 pwt.*

305 Pair of Casters   B.69.1,2

John Burt, 1693–1745
Boston, 1730–1745
MARK: On neck. H. 5½ D. (of base) 1⅞ D. (of lip) 1⅜

Introduced in America about 1700, casters, used at the table for "casting" various spices on food, underwent the same stylistic changes in shape that affected other silver forms. Straight-sided cylinders at first, they assumed by about 1725, the typical Queen Anne pear-shape or baluster form seen here. A later rococo variation in a pair by Burt's son, Benjamin, is at Winterthur.[41] The Bayou Bend examples are the only known pair by the elder Burt; a single larger caster with similar piercings is in the Garvan Collection at Yale University.[42]

41. Fales, *Winterthur Museum*, No. 102.
42. Buhler and Hood, No. 113. The Bayou Bend casters were included in the important 1939 exhibition at Yale University (Phillips, No. 18). The initials *P/SD* on the body have not been identified.

306 Dish B.71.94

Attributed to Daniel You, active ca. 1743–1749/50
Charleston, South Carolina, ca. 1745
MARK: Twice on front scalloped edge. L. 5½
Gift of the Friends of Bayou Bend

This shell-shaped butter dish, an extremely rare American silver form, is suggestive of the close relationship between Charleston silver and furniture and English prototypes.[43]

43. The mark on this dish is thought to be one used by the problematical You (Burton, pp. 201–203). Whether by You or another unidentified maker, the dish is almost certainly American. It has a silver content of slightly less than 90 per cent—typical of American silver—and is marked only with the makers initials. The dish has been published and exhibited (Hammerslough, Vol. 2, p. 85; *Masterpieces of American Silver*, Richmond, Virginia, The Virginia Museum of Fine Arts, 1960, No. 317).

307 Teapot B.69.111

Bartholomew Schaats, 1670–1758
New York, ca. 1728
MARK: On base. H. 6½ D. (of base) 2⅞ L. 10

The small size of early teapots was dictated, in part, by the relative scarcity of the exotic new beverage, tea. Traditional Chinese ceramic forms used for drinking tea were translated by English craftsmen into silver counterparts; American versions of these teapots first appeared in the 1690's. Although a common form in England, American examples of the globular teapot with straight spout survive only as made by a few New York silversmiths.[44] The purity of line and form here is comparable to the famous sugar bowl by Simeon Soumain (1685–1750) in the Garvan Collection at Yale University.[45] Devoid of three-dimensional embellishment, it is typical of Queen Anne period silver. The teapot was originally owned by Sarah Bogert (1728–1781) of New York.[46]

44. Teapots of this type were also made by Jacob Boelen (Miller, *New York Silversmiths*, Pl. IX); Benjamin Wynkoop, Jr. (Peter Bohan and Philip Hammerslough, *Early Connecticut Silver 1700–1840*, Middletown, Conn., Wesleyan University Press, 1970, Pls. 23–24).
45. Buhler and Hood, No. 603
46. Engraved on the base are the initials *SB* and the weight, *18 oz. 6pw*.

308 Teapot
B.69.117

Jonathan Clarke, 1706–1766
Newport and Providence, ca. 1740–1770
MARK: On base. H. 5¾ D. (of base) 3-1/6 L. 9½

Many Massachusetts and Rhode Island silversmiths at mid-eighteenth century favored the floral, mask and geometric pattern of engraving seen around the lid of this teapot.[47]

47. The touchmark on this teapot was misstruck so that Clarke's full name did not register, but it is identical to the mark on No. 342. Several silversmiths with similar names and marks have caused confusion over attribution (Flynt and Fales, pp. 182–185; *Antiques*, March 1971, p. 345).

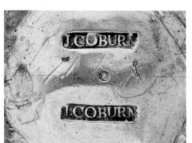

309 Teapot
B.69.113

John Coburn, 1725–1803
Boston, 1765–1785
MARK: Twice on base. H. 6⅜ D. (of base) 3⅛ L. 9½

Stylistic development of the eighteenth century teapot form can be observed in a sequence beginning with the Schaats teapot (No. 307) and followed by the Clarke (No. 308), Coburn (No. 309) and Richardson (No. 310) examples. Coburn is perhaps best known for his teapots and related accessories.[48]

48. Several related pairs or sets of teapots are known (Flynt and Fales, pp. 134–138; Buhler, No. 262). Although slightly earlier, at least in style, these teapots share many of the same distinctive details as the Bayou Bend example. Inscribed on the base is the weight, *20:4*; the later added script initials, *GHLD*; a barely visible name, which appears to be *Doilge*(?).

310 Teapot   B.60.29

Joseph Richardson, 1711–1784
Philadelphia, 1760–1765
MARK: On base. H.6 D. (of base) 2⅞ D. (of lip) 8⅞

This teapot, illustrating the fully developed rococo form, was fashioned by one of Philadelphia's eighteenth century master craftsmen.[49] Although elaborate repoussé designs occur on some contemporary Philadelphia silver, the alternative use of restrained engraved decoration was well suited to a large segment of the city's population influenced by the Quaker preference for simplicity. Apparent in this example is the almost fastidious attention to proportion which characterizes the majority of Philadelphia silver. The cypher *JSM* stands for Joseph and Sarah Morgan of Haddonfield, New Jersey.

49. An identical teapot except for the finial was illustrated (*Antiques*, July 1970, p. 60). The date, *1762*, is engraved on the reverse side of the Bayou Bend teapot.

311 Coffeepot   B.69.95

Nathaniel Hurd, 1729/30–1777
Boston, ca. 1755
MARK: To left of handle and on base.
H.9¾ D. (of base) 4 D. (of lip) 3½ L. 8¼

Far fewer early eighteenth century coffeepots than teapots have survived suggesting coffee was a less popular beverage. In contrast to the short round teapots, the first coffeepots were generally tall and cylindrical, evolving by 1750 into the elongated pear shape of the Queen Anne style. Compared to the prolific production of his father, Jacob (Nos. 282, 283, 314), the silver of Nathaniel Hurd is scarce, and he is more often recognized for his work as an engraver. He is known to have made one other coffeepot which, while similar to this example in form, displays a less successful simple scroll handle and flame finial.[50] The finely engraved rococo coat of arms has been ascribed tentatively to the Mayor family of Boston.[51]

50. Hurd's other coffeepot, engraved with the Stoddard family arms, is in the Fogg Art Museum, Harvard University (*Antiques*, December 1972, p. 966).

51. The arms were used by several families with variations on the name Mayor: Mager or Major, Mayer or Mayor. The same crest is on the opposite side of the body. The weight inscription, *28* (oz)–*4* (dwt.), is scratched on the base.

312 Coffeepot   B.71.75

John Bayly, active ca. 1754–1806
Philadelphia, ca. 1765–1780
MARK: On base. H. 13 D. (of base) 4⁰³⁄₄ D. (of lip) 3³⁄₈

Undoubtedly, the coffeepot was one of the most elegant rococo period designs. This example displays the typical Philadelphia approach to the form, concentrating on line, proportion and attention to carefully placed details, such as the English-derived, but characteristically Philadelphia, bell-shaped finial with spiral gadrooning. It is the only extant coffeepot by Bayly.[52] The touchmark used is unusual both in its incised letters and its combination with a pseudohallmark of two birds in a triangle.

52. The script initials, *ABW*, on the body are purported to be those of a Wickersham family member. See No. 315, for information on Bayly.

313 Tea Canister   B.62.38

Simeon Soumain, 1685–1750
New York, ca. 1728
MARK: On base. H. 5³⁄₁₆ W. 3¹³⁄₁₆ D. 2½

The introduction of tea drinking at the beginning of the eighteenth century necessitated many new accessories. One of these was the tea canister or caddy, a small container for dried tea leaves. The earliest examples of the form were hexagonal, based upon Chinese ceramic prototypes. Only five examples of American tea canisters from the first half of the eighteenth century are known, all of them by New York silversmiths.[53] Originally owned by John (1702–1733) and Marian Morin Scott (m. 1728) of New York, subsequent family owners added the Scott crest, arms, motto and inscription on the base.[54]

53. Other examples are: Simeon Soumain, Metropolitan Museum, New York (Hood, Fig. 101); Thauvet Beasley, active 1727–1757, a pair, Museum of the City of New York (Fales, *Early American Silver*, Fig. 94); Myer Myers, 1723–1795, privately owned (Rosenbaum, p. 137, Pl. 9), this vase-shaped example is probably post 1750; Peter Van Dyck, present location unknown.

54. The later inscription on the base reads *John Scott and Marian Morin/ Married about 1729.* The contemporary letters *S/I*M* are also on the base.

314 Creampot
B.69.112

Jacob Hurd, 1702/03–1758
Boston, 1740–1755
MARK: To left of handle. H. 4 L. 3½

Creampots of the mid-eighteenth century were pear-shaped, had flat-scroll handles, broad pouring lips, and sat on three cabriole feet. Unusual for the period is the elaborate engraving, chasing and punchwork on this creampot. It is one of four examples bearing similarly complex decoration, an apparent specialty of Hurd.[55] While these scenic creampots may be entirely of Jacob Hurd's own creation, it is more probable that he was influenced by Irish and English silver of the 1740–1770 period which often displayed curious rural and farm-yard vignettes.[56] Family tradition states that the three miniature panoramic scenes on this creampot, made for the Providence, Rhode Island, merchant William (1711–1771?) and Mary Aiken Cory, represent "the history of his career."[57]

55. Other similar creampots are at the Cleveland Museum of Art (Acc. No. 40.219); the Yale University Art Gallery (Buhler and Hood, Nos. 149–150).

56. Kurt Ticher, *Irish Silver in the Rococo Period*, Shannon, Ireland, Irish University Press, 1972, Nos. 63–64, 72.

57. The creampot was left by William and Mary Cory to their daughter Rebecca (1746–1825) and son-in-law Nicholas Power, V (1742–1808). It descended in this branch of the family, having the Power name and crest added during the nineteenth century. The house in one of the engraved panels is said to be the Cory's Providence home at the corner of South Main and Transit Streets. The ship is supposedly Cory's sloop, *The Sparrow*. The author is indebted to Mrs. John Chiles for her genealogical research of this piece.

315 Creampot
B.69.100

John Bayly, active ca. 1754–1806
Philadelphia; New Castle County, Delaware, ca. 1750
MARK: On base. H. 4¼ L. (at lip) 4 1/16

Owners initials were commonly engraved on silver. The most elaborate method, popular between 1725 and 1760, used intertwined script letters combined in a mirror-image fashion, called a cypher. The initials *PC* on this creampot, executed in a typically Philadelphia manner, are understood to be those of Phoebe Coates, of Coatesville, Pennsylvania. Several examples of silver, reflecting the same quality of craftsmanship and bearing similar engraving, but stamped with varying touchmarks, are all probably the work of the enigmatic silversmith, John Bayly.[58]

58. Considerable confusion has surrounded the career and marks of John Bayly. He has been identified erroneously as the New York silversmith John Bailey (active ca. 1765–1785), and one of his marks has been misattributed to John Benjamin of Connecticut (1699–1773). Bayly advertised in Philadelphia between 1754 and 1783. It seems likely he "retired" to New Castle County, Delaware, where he is recorded by a land deed (Ruthanna Hindes, "Delaware Silversmiths 1700–1850," *Delaware History*, Vol 12, No. 4, October 1967, pp. 225–256). His estate was inventoried in 1806. Any doubt the Delaware and Philadelphia Bayly were one and the same is dispelled by the 1797 deed which concerned land owned on Front Street, Philadelphia, a former location of Bayly's silver shop. With regard to his marks, his incised surname touch (No. 312) appears together with his initials in a rectangle on a tulip-shaped tankard having initials (*DBC*) engraved similarly to those on the Bayou

Bend creampot (*Antiques*, February 1968, p. 204). An identical creampot with the same manner of cypher (*ABC*?) is known (*Antiques*, December 1969, p. 864), marked with the *IB* in an oval. The use of a mark with his initial and surname within a rectangle is also recorded. On stylistic evidence, the mark on this creampot seems to be one of the first he used (Prime, Nos. 31–37; Buhler and Hood, Nos. 994–995).

316 Sugar Bowl B.69.96

Myer Myers, 1723–1795
New York, 1745–1755
MARK: Center of lid and on base.
H. 4⅛ D. (of lip) 4 D. (of base) 2¹¹⁄₁₆

Although the Chinese never adulterated their tea, it was the English practice to use both sugar and milk. Based upon small Oriental porcelain rice bowls, the first American sugar bowls intended for tea table use were in the Queen Anne style. Circular or octagonal, they had fitted tops with reel handles, which could be inverted and used as small footed trays.[59] Following the same pattern seen in other forms, the reel top continued to be used in New York after it was discarded in other colonies about 1750–1760.[60]

59. The reel-handled top may have been adopted logically from its use on English church silver where paten-covers were used on chalices (Halsey, Nos. 144, 162, 163).

60. A late example by Myers is at Winterthur (Fales, *Winterthur Museum*, No. 112); also Rosenbaum, p. 129; the Bayou Bend sugar bowl is illustrated therein, Pl. 22.

317 Sugar Bowl B.69.109

Paul Revere, II, 1735–1818
Boston, ca. 1765
MARK: On base. H. 6⅛ D. (of base) 3⁵⁄₁₆ D. (of lip) 4¼

In the 1750's, the sugar bowl was first made in an inverted pear shape, while the cover became domed and capped by a finial.[61] The inscription on this bowl, *M. C. to M. T. Q. H.*, stands for Mary Callahan (1776–1855) and her niece Mary Timmins Quincy Hill (1813–1902). It is likely the sugar bowl was owned originally by Mary Callahan's mother, Lucretia Greene Callahan (1748–1824) of Boston or her grandmother, Mary Chandler Greene (d. 1756).

61. Similar finials with cross-hatched detailing appear on Revere coffeepots, a teapot and a sugar bowl, all dated before 1765 (Buhler, Nos. 339, 341, 346, 344). His later pieces employ a different type of pineapple finial, suggesting an early date for this piece. The weight, *13 oz. 12* (dwt.), is scratched on the base.

318 Waste Bowl B.69.98

Paul Revere, 1735–1818
Boston, ca. 1795
MARK: On base. H. 4⁷⁄₁₆ D. (of base) 3⅜ D. (of lip) 5½

The size and shape of this piece suggest it was originally intended as a waste bowl, or receptacle used at the table for the cold tea left in a cup before a fresh one was poured.[62] This double-bellied bowl shape was employed by Revere for a similar pair of cups with handles.[63] Both examples have a mark used in 1795 and possibly later.

62. The unidentified initials *BMF* are on the base of the bowl. The

bowl was exhibited at the Hudson-Fulton Exhibition, Metropolitan Museum, New York (Henry Watson Kent and Florence N. Levy, *Catalogue of an Exhibition of American Paintings, Furniture, Silver and Other Objects of Art, 1625–1825,* New York, 1909, Vol. 2, No. 442).

63. Buhler, No. 404.

319 Tea Tongs   B.69.110
Possibly John Coburn, 1725–1803
Boston, ca. 1750
MARK: None. L. 5

Scissor-like tea tongs were introduced after 1725. This pair was owned by Enoch (b. 1706) and Mary Freeman of Portland, Maine, who are known to have patronized John Coburn. The initials *F/E*M* are engraved inside one of the shell tips.

320 Coffee Set   B.61.11.1–3
Joseph Lownes, active ca. 1780–1816
Philadelphia, 1790–1800

Coffeepot   B.61.11.1
MARK: Same as sugar urn, twice on side of base.
H. 15½ W. (of base) 4¼ D. (of lip) 3¼ L. 11¼

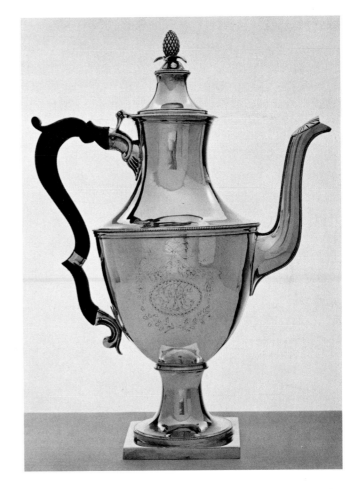

Federal period silver, like Federal furniture, drew inspiration from classical shapes and motifs rather than from actual antique silver prototypes. Geometric forms, uncluttered by relief ornament, were emphasized. Foremost among these in Philadelphia was the urn shape, usually mounted on a square pedestal. This coffeepot illustrates the striking, and appropriately classical, monumentality achieved by Philadelphia silversmiths during the early neoclassical era.[64]

64. This coffeepot is one of the largest, comparable to the John Germon (active ca. 1782–1816) coffeepot, Yale University, the Garvan Collection (Buhler and Hood, No. 899). The Bayou Bend service was owned by the Da Costa family of Philadelphia. The bright-cut initials *JDC*, probably indicating a Da Costa family member, are unidentified.

Sugar Urn   B.61.11.2
MARK: On base. H. 10¼ W. (of base) 3⁵⁄₁₆ D. (of lip) 4⁷⁄₁₆

Matching tea and coffee services, including a creampot, sugar bowl and/or waste bowl, were uncommon until the last quarter of the eighteenth century.

Waste Bowl   B.61.11.3
MARK: Same as sugar urn, twice on base.
H. 5½ W. (of base) 3½ D. (of lip) 6⅛

321 Creampot   B.61.11.4
Philadelphia, 1790–1800
MARK: Unmarked. H. 7 W. (of base) 2½ L. 4½

Despite appearing similar to the preceding coffeepot,
sugar urn and waste bowl (No. 320) and being purchased cur-
rently with them, this creampot is not original to the Lownes
coffee service. It bears the differing script initials, *RRB*.

322 Tea Set   B.67.5.1-4
Standish Barry, 1763–1844
Baltimore, Maryland, 1784–1800
Gift of Tiffany and Company

Teapot   B.67.5.1
MARK: On side of base. H. 11⅞ W. (of base) 3⁹⁄₁₆ L. 10½

Although pierced galleries and beading are usually associated with Philadelphia Federal silver, they occur here on a
Baltimore tea service. In contrast to the heavy quality in Barry's
designs, commented on by his biographers, the proportions of
this service are well conceived.[65] The urn shape and high neck
of many tea and coffeepots meant that the lid could no longer
be hinged to the body.

65. J. Hall Pleasants and Howard Sill, *Maryland Silversmiths, 1715–
1830*, Baltimore, privately printed, 1930, p. 96.

Sugar Urn
B.67.5.2

MARK: Same as teapot on side of base.
H. 11   W. (of base) 3 5⁄16   D. (of lip) 4⅞

The contemporary script initials *EW*, which appear on each piece in this set, are unidentified.

Creampot
B.67.5.3

MARK: Four times on the base.
H. 7¼   W. (of base) 2 7⁄16   L. 5⅞

The usual helmet-shaped creampot (No. 321) has been replaced in this service with an urn design echoing that of the teapot and sugar urn. Also uncommon is the cover, a feature peculiar to a few Philadelphia and New York examples.[66] The teapot-like pouring spout, however, is unique.

66. Hood, Nos. 176–177.

Sugar Tongs
B.67.5.4

MARK: Same as teapot, twice on inside of bow.   L. 6⅛

During the Federal period, sugar or tea tongs were cut from a single sheet of silver and hammered into a bow shape which tapered to the grips, in this instance, acorn shaped.

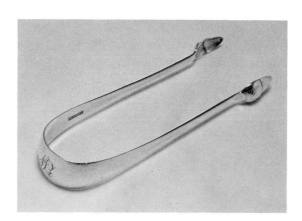

323 Tea Set   B.66.4.1–3
Henry Lupp, 1760–1800
New Brunswick, New Jersey, 1783–1800

Teapot   B.66.4.1
MARK: On base. H.9¼ W. (of base) 3½ L.9¾

The amount and combination of ornament belie the rural provenance of this tea set. Beading, pierced galleries and the placement of the pieces diagonally on their bases indicate the strong influence of Philadelphia upon an extensive surrounding area. The set was owned by Brigadier General Anthony (1750–1803) and Margaret Ellis (1768–1850) White of New Brunswick, whose initials appear within an elaborate bright-cut ornamental device on the body.[67]

67. This set is illustrated in Margaret E. White, *The Decorative Arts of Early New Jersey*, Princeton, New Jersey, D. Van Nostrand Company, Inc., 1964, p. 78.

Sugar Urn   B.66.4.2
MARK: Same as teapot, on base.
H.9⅛ W. (of base) 3⅜ D. (of lip) 4⅞

Bright-cut ornament, a type of engraving consisting of short, noncontinuous gouges, was widely used during the neoclassical period and is well illustrated on this sugar urn.[68] The light, delicate effect achieved was in keeping with the spirit of the overall design. Bows, floral garlands and pendants were the most widely used bright-cut motifs.

68. The weight, *18 oz.—12 dwt.*, is scratched on the base.

Creampot   B.66.4.3
MARK: Same as teapot, on base.
H.6½ W. (of base) 2⅞ L. 5¼

Like the other pieces in this set, the creampot has its original weight scratched on the base: *6 oz.—12 dwt.*

324 Teapot

B.69.256.1

Attributed to Joseph Loring, 1743–1815
Boston, ca. 1797
MARK: None. H.6⅞ W.4¾ L.11⅜
Gift of Mrs. Ernst Auerbach in memory of
Ernst Auerbach

A history of family ownership, together with stylistic similarities to documented pieces of silver, strongly suggest that Joseph Loring made this teapot, two creampots (Nos. 325, 327) and a sugar bowl (No. 326) also in the Bayou Bend Collection, although all are unmarked.[69]

Reeded banding was frequently used by Loring and other Boston silversmiths. The squared handle and ball feet, newly introduced features, reflected the influence of the English Regency phase of neoclassicism.[70] A technical innovation employed in making this teapot was the time-saving use of machine-rolled sheet silver which was simply bent and seamed, at the juncture with the handle, to form the body.

69. The exact line of descent of this teapot and Nos. 325, 326 and 327 is unknown, although they are said to have been made for and passed on to Loring family members. Being made for the family would help explain why they are unmarked. Two spoons, which accompanied these pieces and which are similarly engraved, confirm an attribution to Loring, being marked by him (Nos. 344, 345). The bright-cut initials *ML* on Nos. 325 and 326 possibly stand for Mary Atkins Loring, wife of the silversmith. The significance of the date *1797* is not known. The teapot bears the following inscriptions, all added at a later date: *John Hall/ to Susan Loring; SHL/1797; MHL/to JES/1883/JES to/JS/1901.*

70. Buhler, Nos. 433, 440.

325 Creampot

B.69.256.2

Attributed to Joseph Loring, 1743–1815
Boston, ca. 1797
MARK: None. H.5 W.3 L.5¼
Gift of Mrs. Ernst Auerbach in memory of
Ernst Auerbach

The distinctive ribbon and oval bright-cut ornamental device on this creampot, similar to that on No. 326, was used in a modified form by Loring on a set of four two-handled covered cups for the Brattle Street Church, Boston.[71]

71. Buhler, No. 433; Buhler and Hood, No. 275. The script initials *MHL to JES*, engraved at a later date, are beneath the bright-cut device. For provenance, see No. 324.

326 Sugar Bowl

B.69.256.3

Attributed to Joseph Loring, 1743–1815
Boston, ca. 1797
MARK: None. H.5⅜ W.4⅛ L.6⅞
Gift of Mrs. Ernst Auerbach in memory of
Ernst Auerbach

Despite the similarity of the preceding teapot and creampot to this sugar bowl, it is clear they were not intended as a matching set.[72]

72. The initials *MHL to JES*, engraved at a later date, are beneath the bright-cut device. For provenance, see No. 324.

327 Creampot
B.69.256.4

Attributed to Joseph Loring, 1743–1815
Boston, ca. 1797
MARK: None. H.4 ¹⁵⁄₁₆ W. 3 L.5 ⁵⁄₁₆
Gift of Mrs. Ernst Auerbach in memory of
Ernst Auerbach

Stylistic similarities and almost identical inscriptions indicate this creampot was intended as a mate to the teapot (No. 324).[73]

73. The block letters *SH* are on the base: *MHL/to/JES/1883/JES/to/JS/1901* and *SHL/1797* are engraved in script on the body.

328 Teapot and Stand
B.69.167.1,2

Amos Whitney, active ca. 1800
New York, ca. 1805
MARK: On base of teapot and back of stand.
H. 8⅜ W. 5⅜ L. 12⅜

Classical "boat-shaped" forms appeared in American silver at the end of the eighteenth century. At first taut-lined and delicate (No. 324), by 1800 they had assumed a more rotund aspect in anticipation of the heavier Empire style. The boat shape was handled with particular skill by New York silversmiths, especially in the design of teapots. For both functional and aesthetic reasons, the flat-bottomed teapot was often accompanied by a matching silver stand.[74]

74. The unidentified initials *ELH* are on both teapot and stand.

329 Tea and Coffee Set
B.71.89.1–7

Samuel Kirk, 1792–1872
Baltimore, Maryland, 1824–1827
Gift of Miss Ima Hogg and the Friends of Bayou Bend

Coffeepot
B.71.89.1

MARK: On base. H. 12⅞ W. (of base) 5⅞ L. 12⅞

The second, or Empire, phase of neoclassical silver design emphasized massive bulbous shapes, accented by bold cast feet, finials, spouts and handles. Closely paralleling the motifs of French-inspired Empire furniture (Nos. 184, 196), winged paw feet, animal heads and acanthus leaves were commonly employed. The gauge or thickness of the silver was generally heavier than before, and machine-milled borders and banding were frequently used. When these elements were judiciously combined, as in this tea and coffee set, the result was a vigorous and impressive statement.

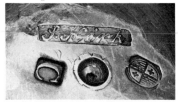

Teapot   B.71.89.2

MARK: Same as coffeepot, on base.
H. 11½ W. (of base) 5¼ L. 11⅞

Identical spouts, handles and finials were used by Kirk on another tea and coffee service, datemarked 1824, but they are far less successfully integrated with the body.[75] Although the high-relief floral band used on this teapot and on the other articles in the set is machine stamped, the echoing grape and leaf pattern on the lid is executed in repoussé. It is one of the earliest reintroductions of this technique in nineteenth century American silver and presages its popularity during the rococo revival (No. 331).

75. *Samuel Kirk and Son: American Silver Craftsmen since 1815*, Chicago Historical Society, 1966, No. IX. The Bayou Bend service is one of Kirk's finest efforts in the neoclassical mode.

Teapot   B.71.89.3

MARK: Same as coffeepot, on base.
H. 11¼ W. (of base) 5 L. 11⅜

Sugar Bowl   B.71.89.4

MARK: Same as coffeepot, on base.
H. 9⅛ W. (of base) 5 D. 8

The Baltimore Assay Office was established in 1814, by an act of the Maryland legislature.[76] Based upon the English system of hallmarking and regulating the silver content of objects, the Baltimore law differed in allowing a standard slightly lower than sterling.[77] All silver was required to be marked with the name or initials of the silversmith, the arms of the State of Maryland and a dominical letter, which indicated the year in which the article was made. The large C marking this set of silver was used in 1824, but since no marks have been identified for the years 1825–1827, it is assumed that the C was used during this period also.

76. The law was enacted January 29, 1814, and was supplemented January 30, 1815. It was modified in 1830 (see No. 331).

77. The law specified that 11 ounces out of 12 must be pure silver. The sterling standard is 11 ounces 2 pennyweights.

Creampot   B.71.89.5

MARK: Same as coffeepot, on base.
H. 7½ W. (of base) 3¾ L. 6⅜

Waste Bowl   B.71.89.6

MARK: Same as coffeepot, on base.
H. 5¾ W. (of base) 4¹⁵⁄₁₆ D. (of bowl) 8¼

Tea Tongs   B.71.89.7

MARK: Same as coffeepot, inside bow. L. 6¾

330 Tea Set   B.65.13.1-3

William Gale, Jacob Wood and Jasper Hughes,
active ca. 1824–1850
Charles Hyde and James Goodrich, active 1817–1861
New Orleans, Louisiana, 1824–1840

Teapot   B.65.13.1
MARK: On base. H. 10⅞ D. (of base) 4¾ L. 12

The foremost supplier of silver and jewelry in New
Orleans and the lower Mississippi River Valley during the first
half of the nineteenth century was the partnership of Hyde and
Goodrich. Much of what they sold, however, was made by
other local silversmiths (No. 333) or imported. This tea set
bears Hyde and Goodrich's mark but also has the pseudo-
hallmarks used by the New York silversmithing firm of Gale,
Wood and Hughes. The bulbous melon shapes are typically
Empire, but the lack of specific classical ornament indicates the
possible influence of the plainer French Restauration style.[78]

78. Information supplied with the purchase of this set indicated it has
been divided up by the family.

Sugar Bowl   B.65.13.2
MARK: On base. H. 10½ D. (of base) 4 D. (of lip) 4¼

A common feature of nineteenth century tea and coffee
sets is that the component pieces, like this sugar bowl, reiterate
the shape of the tea or coffee pot. Even the chunky flattened
disc finial reflects the shape and horizontal stance of the bowl.

Waste Bowl   B.65.13.3
MARK: Same as sugar bowl, on base.
H. 5¾ D. (of base) 4⅜ D. (of lip) 7

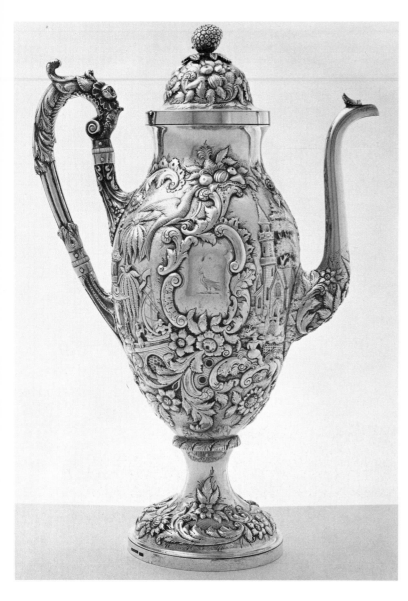

331   Tea and Coffee Set   B.69.525.1–4
Andrew Ellicott Warner, 1786–1870
Baltimore, Maryland, 1835–1850

Coffeepot   B.69.525.1
MARK: On side of base. H. 15¾ D. (of base) 5 L. 10½

The ultimate expression of the rococo revival is represented in this tea and coffee set.[79] Extravagantly florid repoussé
designs were *au courant* at mid-century, but Baltimore silversmiths like Samuel Kirk (No. 329) and Andrew E. Warner
specialized in eclectic fantasy landscapes where elements of the
gothic, Oriental and Moorish tastes were often combined in
the exotic architecture depicted. Similar themes were carried
out contemporarily in architectural and furniture design.

79. Presumably the set originally had a sugar bowl. The crest and
letter *L*, which appears on each piece of silver, has not been identified.

Waste Bowl   B.69.525.4
MARK: Same as coffeepot, on side of base.
H. 7¹⁵⁄₁₆ D. (of base) 5 D. (of lip) 7¼

Teapot

B.69.525.2

MARK: Same as coffeepot, on side of base and inside base rim. H. 14⅛ D. (of base) 4½ L. 9¾

Beginning in 1830, the testing and marking of silver by the Baltimore Assay Office was no longer required by law (No. 329).[80] It was necessary, however, for the individual silversmiths to indicate the amount of pure silver in ounces and pennyweights per pound troy (12 ounces) on all silver offered for sale. The stamped numbers *11²*, which accompany Warner's name mark, indicate that the silver content is 92.5 per cent or equivalent to the sterling standard.

80. The exact date was February 5, 1830.

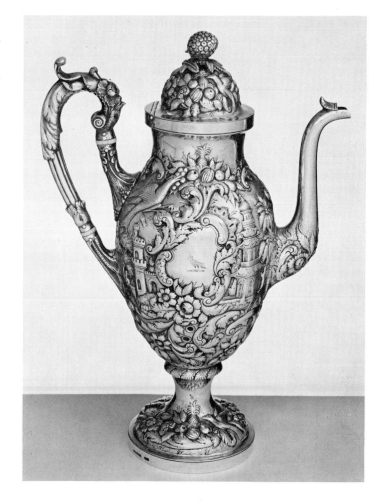

Creampot

B.69.525.3

MARK: Same as coffeepot, on side of base.
H. 9⅞ D. (of base) 3¼ L. 5½

332 Pair of Ewers   B.67.1,2

J. T. Bailey and Andrew B. Kitchen,
active ca. 1833–1846
Philadelphia, ca. 1833–1846
MARK: On base. H. 19 D. (of base) 5¼ L. 9⁹⁄₁₆

These large ewers, probably presentation pieces, display a subtly successful blending of neoclassical and rococo styles. The form is basically antique with classical acanthus leaf and applied mask decoration, although the pyriform body recalls mid-eighteenth century shapes. Rococo in spirit are the elaborately scrolled handle with playful putti, the meandering flowered vine and the diapered reserve, similar to that used on rococo period furniture (No. 110).[81]

81. The script initials *TSHF* appear in a cartouche beneath the spout.

333 Goblet   B.70.50

Charles Christian Küchler and Adolph Himmel,
1852–1853
New Orleans, Louisiana, 1852–1853
MARK: *K.* and *H.* in Roman capitals and *HYDE AND GOODRICH* (No. 334) on base of cup of goblet.
H. 7⁷⁄₁₆ D. (of base) 3⁷⁄₁₆ D. (of lip) 3½

By 1800 the goblet was no longer regarded as predominantly a church form. Increasingly it was made for domestic use, individually or in sets, often to accompany a pitcher. This goblet bears the marks of two firms and represents a prevalent nineteenth century practice of one shop, in this case Hyde and Goodrich (Nos. 330, 334), retailing silver made by other silversmiths.[82]

82. Similar examples marked by Küchler and Himmel are discussed (*Antiques*, July 1973, p. 88; Warren, Fig. F-5-A). The location of the touchmarks on the base of the cup of the Bayou Bend goblet precluded their being photographed.

334 Cup   B.68.2

Charles Hyde and James Goodrich, active 1817–1861
New Orleans, Louisiana, 1835–1845
MARK: On base. H. 3⅞ D. (of base) 3⅛ D. (of lip) 3⅛
Gift of James Craig

Small silver cups were one of the forms most frequently made during the nineteenth century. Often, these cups were given as awards or tokens of appreciation. Repoussé and chased floral, leaf and vine motifs were universally used between 1835 and 1875. The chaste neoclassical anthemion banding around the base of this cup, however, suggests an early date in this style.[83]

83. The unidentified script initials *SHD* are on the front of the cup. It has been published (Warren, Fig. F-5-E).

335 Cup (one of a pair)   B.59.13.2

Asa Blanchard, active ca. 1808–1839
Lexington, Kentucky, ca. 1820
MARK: On base. H. 3⅜ D. (of base) 2¹¹⁄₁₆ D. (of lip) 3

Small cups without handles were so prevalent in the southern states during the nineteenth century that they have become known as mint julep cups. Undoubtedly they served a multitude of purposes.[84]

84. Exhibited in *Southern Silver*, The Museum of Fine Arts, Houston, 1968 (Warren, Fig. E-2-C).

336 Cup   B.57.73

Peter L. Krider, active ca. 1850
Philadelphia, ca. 1850
MARK: On base. H. 3¾ D. (of base) 2½ D. (of lip) 3⁵⁄₁₆

The importation of silver from northern cities for sale in southern shops was a common nineteenth century practice (Nos. 330, 339). This cup, made by Krider in Philadelphia was additionally marked by the Louisville, Kentucky, retailer, Joseph Werne, Sr. (1808–1858), or his son, Joseph, Jr. (1837–1905).[85]

85. In script letters on the side of the cup is the name *Zorn*. Exhibited in *Southern Silver*, The Museum of Fine Arts, Houston, 1968 (Warren, Fig. E-10-A).

337 Cup (one of a set of eight)   B.57.74.7

Scovil, Willey and Co., active 1815–1836
Cincinnati, Ohio, ca. 1815–1836
MARK: On base. H. 3⁷⁄₁₆ D. (of base) 2½ D. (of lip) 2⅞

The script initials *AGJ* are on the side of the cup.

338 Cup (one of a pair)   B.57.72.2

David Kinsey, active 1817–1860 *or*
Edward Kinsey, active ca. 1834–1850 *or*
F. Kinsey, active ca. 1837
Cincinnati, Ohio, ca. 1817–1860
MARK: On base. H. 3⁹⁄₁₆ D. (of base) 2⁵⁄₁₆ D. (of lip) 2⅞

The script initials *EC* are on the side of the cup.

339 Cup   B.73.10

Gregg, Hayden and Company, 1846–1852
Charleston, South Carolina, 1846–1852
MARK: On base. H. 3⅛ D. (of base) 2⅛ D. (of lip) 2¹³⁄₁₆

The popular reappearance of the octagonal shape in American silver occurred approximately one hundred years after its use in the Queen Anne period. This design appears in cups and occasionally in other forms.[86] Although the cup is marked by the firm of H. Sidney Hayden, Augustus H. Hayden and William Gregg, it is thought that they operated only a retail jewelry shop, importing most of their stock from northern cities and England.[87]

86. *Antiques*, March 1971, p. 410, illustrates a handsome tea service by James Conning (active ca. 1825–1870) which must have owed its inspiration, at least indirectly, to Queen Anne silver. Octagonally shaped cups, of course, were not an eighteenth century form. The initials *CPSJ*, which are on this cup's front panel, are unidentified.

87. This firm underwent five changes of name and partnerships between 1838 and 1863. For a complete discussion, see Burton, pp. 85–86.

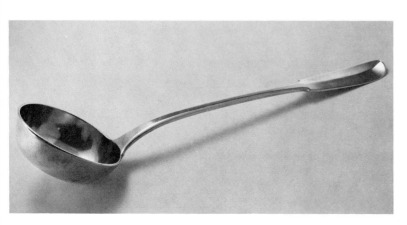

340   Ladle   B.71.93

Pierre Lamothe, active ca. 1810–1823
New Orleans, Louisiana, ca. 1815
MARK: On back of handle. L. 13½
Gift of the Friends of Bayou Bend

Examples of silver by Lamothe seem virtually non-existent. This ladle is the largest extant piece known.[88]

88. "A Gift of Southern Silver," *Bulletin*, The Museum of Fine Arts, Houston, Vol. 3, No. 2, April 1972, pp. 19–20.

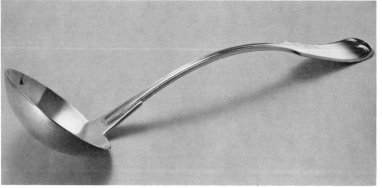

341   Ladle   B.67.34

Charles Hyde and James Goodrich, active 1817–1861
New Orleans, Louisiana, ca. 1835–1850
MARK: On back of handle. L. 13¼

342 Tablespoon   B.73.14
Jonathan Clarke, 1706–1766
Newport and Providence, Rhode Island, ca. 1750
MARK: On back of handle. L.7¾

Handle, with upturned rounded end and long midrib, tapered to oval bowl with long rattail; *A*S* on back of handle.

343 Teaspoon (one of twelve)   B.66.5.1–12
Henry Lupp, 1760–1800
New Brunswick, New Jersey, ca. 1785
MARK: On back of handle.
Gift of Dr. Royall Calder

Handle, with bright-cut-decorated rounded end, tapering to pointed, oval bowl with rounded drop; script initials *IIB* on front of handle.[89]

89. The initials stand for John and Johanna White Bayard of Philadelphia.

344 Tablespoon   B.69.256.5
Joseph Loring, 1743–1815
Boston, ca. 1797
MARK: On back of handle. L.9⅛
Gift of Mrs. Ernst Auerbach in memory of
Ernst Auerbach

Downturned handle, rounded end and oval bowl with rounded drop. Engraved in script letters on front of handle, *SH/1797*; on back of handle, *MHL/to/SH/1883*. This spoon has a provenance similar to No. 324.

345 Dessert Spoon   B.69.256.6
Joseph Loring, 1743-1815
Boston, ca. 1797
MARK: On back of handle. L.7⅛
Gift of Mrs. Ernst Auerbach in memory of
Ernst Auerbach

Downturned handle, rounded end and oval bowl with rounded drop. Engraved script letters on front of handle, *SL/to HHL*. For provenance, see No. 324.

346 Teaspoon (one of five)   B.66.23.1–5
John Shaw, active ca. 1802–1819
Newport, Rhode Island, ca. 1815
MARK: On back of handle. L.5½
Gift of Mr. Ralph Carpenter

Downturned handle with "coffin" end tapered to pointed, oval bowl; script initials *BHP* engraved on front of handle.

347 Teaspoon (one of two)   B.67.8.1–2

John Campbell, b. 1803
Fayetteville, North Carolina, ca. 1830–1840
MARK: On back of handle. L.6⅛
Gift of Dr. and Mrs. Benjamin Caldwell

"Fiddle" handle with upturned rounded end, tapered to shoulder above pointed, oval bowl; *EUBANKS* in script letters on front of handle.

348 Teaspoon (one of six)   B.62.34.1–6

Edward and David Kinsey, ca. 1836–1850
Cincinnati, Ohio, ca. 1840
MARK: On back of handle. L.5¾

"Fiddle" handle with upturned rounded end, tapered to shoulder above pointed, oval bowl; script initials *ACG* on front of handle.

349 Teaspoon   B.72.4

Fred H. Clark and Co., active 1840–1860
Memphis, Tennessee, ca. 1850
MARK: On back of handle. L.5¾
Gift of Dr. and Mrs. Benjamin Caldwell

"Fiddle" handle with downturned rounded end, tapered to shoulder above pointed, oval bowl.

350 Teaspoon   B.72.3

William H. Calhoun, active 1839–1860
Nashville, Tennessee, ca. 1850
MARK: On back of handle. L.7
Gift of Dr. and Mrs. Benjamin Caldwell

"Fiddle" handle with upturned rounded end, tapered to shoulder above pointed, oval bowl.

351 Teaspoon   B.72.5

Samuel Musgrove, active 1850–1860
Nashville, Tennessee, ca. 1850
MARK: On back of handle. L.5¾
Gift of Dr. and Mrs. Benjamin Caldwell

"Fiddle" handle with upturned rounded end, tapered to shoulder above pointed, oval bowl.

352 **Tablespoon**   B.72.2

James E. Merriman, active ca. 1845–1860 *or*
C. G. Merriman, active ca. 1850–1851
Memphis, Tennessee, ca. 1850
MARK: On back of handle. L. 8⅜
Gift of Dr. and Mrs. Benjamin Caldwell

"Fiddle" handle with upturned rounded end, tapered to shoulder above pointed, oval bowl.

353 **Tablespoon (one of six)**   B.69.400.1–6

Adolph Himmel, active ca. 1854–1875
New Orleans, Louisiana, ca. 1860
MARK: On back of handle. L. 8⅜

"Fiddle thread" handle with upturned rounded end, tapered to shoulder above pointed, oval bowl; script initials *EC* on front of handle.

354 **Tablespoon**   B.68.1

Fred Allen and Co., active ca. 1870
Galveston, Texas, ca. 1870
MARK: On back of handle. L. 8⅜
Gift of Robert Ensko, Inc.

"Fiddle thread" handle with upturned rounded end, tapered to shoulder above pointed, oval bowl.

355 **Fork (one of six)**   B.69.399.1–6

Louis Muh, active ca. 1823–1854
New Orleans, Louisiana, ca. 1840
MARK: On back of handle. L. 8⅜

"Fiddle thread" handle with upturned rounded end, tapered to four tines; script initial *L* on front of handle.

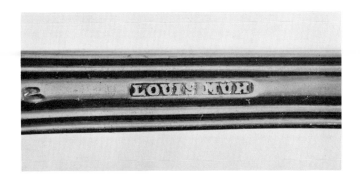

Index

(Illustration numbers are printed in boldface type.)

Designed by Bert Clarke and Robert C. Lewis.
Composed in English Monotype Bembo
and printed at the Press of A. Colish
in Mount Vernon, N.Y.
Binding by Publishers Book Bindery, New York, N.Y.